MW00533127

THE
WOLFBERRY
CHRONICLE

AND OTHER PERMIAN
BASIN TALES FROM THE
HENRY OIL COMPANY

GREGORY BERKHOUSE

Ebook: 978-1-7331869-4-0
Paperback: 978-1-7331869-5-7
Hardback: 978-1-7331869-6-4

AUTHOR'S NOTES

Jim Henry is a man blessed with two first names, and he also named his oil company Henry. So, to avoid confusion, I call the man by his first name, and I refer to the oil company as Henry. Besides, I know Jim; he is my friend, and it would feel pretentious to call him by his last name. As most of the other people in the book are also my friends, or at the least my acquaintances, for the same reason I call them by their first names, except when there are complicating factors. For example, Henry Groppe, once introduced by his full name, must become Groppe. And when Dennis Johnson is talking with Dennis Phelps, they must for the moment be Johnson and Phelps.

Oil is a technical industry. I wanted to make this book interesting and understandable to readers who don't have a petroleum background, but without compromising the technical accuracy. One of my guiding principles in writing was: *accessible to the non-technical, inoffensive to the technical.* To that end, I have provided brief explanations of most of the technical terms and concepts. I have also devoted a few "pull-over" chapters to more fundamental technical matters in the story: it would have been impossible to sprinkle in enough information about fracs, horizontal drilling and Permian Basin geology to give the reader context, while still preserving the flow of the narrative.

That said, I wanted to address a few technical matters here at the outset, beginning with our abbreviations for volumes and producing rates, which I use throughout. The basic unit of *volume* for *oil* is a 42-gallon *barrel*, abbreviated BO, and for *gas* it's *one thousand cubic feet* (at standard temperature and pressure), abbreviated MCFG. By the way, in the petroleum industry, to denote *one thousand* we use *M* from the Latin *mille*, rather than *K* from the Greek *kilo*. When we describe *cumulative produced volumes*, whether during a month or over the lifetime of a well, we generally speak in terms of *thousands of barrels of oil*, abbreviated MBO, and *millions of cubic feet of gas*, abbreviated MMCFG (*MM is one thousand thousands*, or one million). For reference, a good *vertical* Permian Basin Wolfcamp well makes at least 100 MBO and 200 MMCFG over its lifetime, and a good two-mile *horizontal* makes maybe 750 MBO and 1500 MMCFG (or 1.5 BCFG, where B signifies billion). We describe *producing rates* in *daily* terms: *barrels of oil per day*, abbreviated BOPD, and *thousands of cubic feet of gas per day*, MCFGD; 120 BOPD and 250 MCFGD is a good initial rate for a vertical Wolfcamp well, and 1000 BOPD and 2000 MCFGD for a horizontal.

Also, there is the expression of *energy equivalence*. One barrel of oil yields about the same amount of energy as six thousand cubic feet of gas: 1 BO equals 6 MCFG. For convenience, we often combine the oil and gas volumes into a single unit of measure, called *oil equivalents* (note the different word) and abbreviated OE, by using that ratio. For example, a well that is producing 100 BOPD and 180 MCFGD is making 130 BOEPD, and one that cumulatively produced 300 MBO and 600 MMCFG yielded 400 MBOE.

Finally, most Permian Basin reservoirs that produce oil also produce what we call *associated gas*. Gas is dissolved in oil similarly to CO_2 dissolved in Coke (except in oil it happens naturally). When you relieve the pressure on the oil by bringing it to the surface, much of the gas is liberated, just as CO_2 foams up in the glass when you pour your Coke. The produced oil and gas are separated at the surface and processed differently.

I hope you enjoy the read.

CONTENTS

Author's Notes iii
Prologue: So What's the Story Here?. 1
Chapter 1: The Wonder Years. 5
Chapter 2: A Little Ol' Spraberry Driller 23
Chapter 3: Permian Basin Rocks for Jocks 35
Chapter 4: From Austin to Appalachia. 49
Chapter 5: Henry Petroleum Version 2.0 62
Chapter 6: The Executive Office. 80
Chapter 7: MIPs, Flips and Floods. 98
Chapter 8: What Is a Frac?. 147
Chapter 9: Another Dennis 164
Chapter 10: Setting the Wolfberry Stage 173
Chapter 11: Birth of the Wolfberry 182
Chapter 12: Growth Ballistic 196
Chapter 13: Departures 214
Chapter 14: Concho 226
Chapter 15: Transitions 243
Chapter 16: The Horizontal World 259
Chapter 17: Henry Goes Sideways. 267
Epilogue: Now We Are Fifty-Two. 280
Author's Acknowledgements. 283
Author Bio. 285

Prologue
So What's the Story Here?

On November 1, 2019, Jim and Paula Henry's oil company turned fifty.

That's a big deal for any company, but especially for one that began as a mom-and-pop shop without any capital. And their company has not only survived but thrived in a commodity-based industry with volatile pricing. Henry is still going strong today and is still family owned. So the Henrys' half-century is a big deal.

As a continuing part of their fiftieth anniversary celebration, Jim and Paula wanted a book about the history of their oil company and its success. They asked me to write it for two reasons. First, I have worked at Henry for twenty of its fifty years, so I personally know the company and its people, employees, partners and service providers. And second, I am a geologist and an engineer. Henry is a technical company in a technical industry, and its history needs a technical teller.

There is one rather important qualification I do not have: I am not a writer. But two out of three ain't bad. And besides, I thought,

1

history is straight forward enough—a lot of dates, numbers and names. I figured I could pull that off.

But of course, history is much more than dates and numbers and names. History is at heart a story, a tale, and Jim and Paula wanted *their* tale told. They wanted a book not merely about their company's statistics but about its soul, its personality, its maturing in wisdom and in stature through the years.

I knew there must be a profound story here, and I knew at least some of its components. Henry hires smart people. But there are smart people at a lot of companies, and most companies don't achieve what Henry has achieved. And everybody knows about Jim and Paula's generosity, their great benevolence to their employees and their community. That's uncommon practice, and it must be important to the story. But no actual mechanism in benevolence could, by itself, bring about such material and measurable success. There had to be other gears in the box.

So I interviewed a lot of key players in Henry's history—more than forty folks from inside and outside the company, more than seventy hours of conversations, and untold email inquiries and follow-up texts. I asked questions, and I let them tell their tales. They talked, and I listened. I learned a lot—such is the reward of listening.

I expected to hear about wild wells. Henry is an oil company, after all—we drill wells, and wells can get wild. I also expected to hear about the getting of great wealth. As I said, Jim and Paula started their company with no capital—the only thing in Jim's wallet then was a business card. But between 2006 and 2010, they conducted three asset sales that made their company a billion dollars. That's *billion*, with a *b*. So I expected to hear about wild wells and great wealth gotten, and I did. This is all good, because Jim wanted the book to be exciting, and it's hard to make dates and numbers and names exciting.

Most books and movies about oil include wild wells and great wealth. The problem is that many of them stop right there: blow-outs and riches, The End. And while wild wells do sometimes establish a company's success, they sometimes cause its demise. And great wealth is the result of success, not the cause. So the Henry story must have a firmer soul.

As I listened to my interviewees, a common theme emerged—sometimes explicit, sometimes half-hidden in the background. Sometimes I didn't see it until I tied together two or three testimonies. The theme is very simple and yet very profound: *favor given and received.* The cause of Henry's great success is not only that Jim and Paula themselves have been so benevolent, so ethical and of such bright character, but also that their company has collaborated with kindred spirits, folks of similar stuff, and received good from them in turn. Henry hired quality people and treated them well, and those people worked hard for Henry. Henry's employees selected vendors and service providers of the same ilk, and all parties did right by each other. The Henry field team took care of their landowners' properties, and the landowners expressed their gratitude in fair terms. Henry management identified investors and business partners with similar priorities and dealt with them equitably, and partners of the same sort sought out Henry. And as Midland helped Henry to prosper, Jim and Paula gave back to the community many times over.

Of course, not all the company's relationships worked well, and none was perfect—many were difficult, and a few were downright disasters. But overwhelmingly, favor and fairness were exchanged.

So you will see, if you read on, a story of reciprocal trust and requited respect, of goodness and gratitude manifested in both directions, of the company and its relations doing unto each other as they would have the other do unto them.

The Henry story is a tale of mutual goodwill.

(And of wild wells and the getting of great wealth.)

Chapter 1
The Wonder Years

THE CARICATURE OF a petroleum engineer is a rectilinear guy or gal religiously devoted to calculation: he gathers his numbers, pours them libation-like into the Almighty Equation, and bows unquestioningly to the output. He is spellbound by spreadsheets, and he balances his checkbook to three decimal places. He struggles with the concept of concept. His safe place is the Binary—*on* and *off, yes* and *no, black* and *white*; indeterminants like *gray* and *maybe* disquiet him. To such a one, all unknowns are negative, and every risk anathema.

Jim Henry is a petroleum engineer. But he is not *that* petroleum engineer. Jim can calculate, equate and evaluate with the best of them, but he also gets that not all things can be measured. Some things must be imagined—in some situations, some amount of risk and uncertainty is acceptable. Especially when the potential gain is great.

In late 1969, ten years into his professional petroleum career at age 35, Jim encountered an unanticipated crossroads and had to make a major vocational decision. Being a good engineer, he first identified the options, listed the pros and cons of each and assessed their relative merits. One option presented significant risk and correspondingly great reward. But there were too many unknowns, and he was unable to quantify its value. So Jim departed from the caricature engineer: he quit calculating and gave over to imagining.

From the time he was a young teenager, Jim knew that he was fashioned to be an engineer. In elementary school he had done poorly in spelling because he was taught by memorization rather than phonics; as Jim said, "I'm a rules guy, and so I struggled." But in junior high he encountered algebra and excelled at it, and later he mastered geometry and trigonometry. "I found out then and there that I had an analytical mind for subjects like math, and so I knew in junior high that I wanted to be an engineer." Jim had no doubt inherited some of his ciphering skills from his father, James, who had also chosen engineering as his profession (although in mining rather than petroleum).

Early in his collegiate career, Jim established a straightforward professional goal: he wanted to be the head of a good oil company. And he sketched out a path to get him there. "I had a plan when I was graduating from college. I wanted to work for a major [a large oil company] because they had the best training. Then I wanted to move to a smaller company and climb through the ranks and end up running it. That was my Plan A." Jim qualified himself academically for his goal by obtaining bachelor's and master's degrees in petroleum engineering from the University of Oklahoma, where he also enrolled in the Air Force ROTC program. After graduating in May 1958, he served two years as a second lieutenant in the Air Force, working as a research officer at Wright-Patterson AFB in Dayton in its Propulsion Laboratory, Fluids and Lubricants Division.

Jim then entered the petroleum industry and began walking out his plan. He rejoined Humble Oil and Refining Company, where he had interned while writing his master's thesis prior to enlistment. "The cream of the crop of all the companies that were interviewing at OU was Humble Oil. Everybody wanted to go to work for Humble, not only because they were a great company but because they also had a great training program." Humble initially assigned Jim to its Monahans District in West Texas, then, a few months later, sent him to Houston for a tour in the production department computing group, where he also enrolled in the company's reservoir engineering school. A year later, Humble transferred him to the Midland office, where he worked in engineering computing.

Jim finally got his hands oily in the Andrews District, in June 1963, where he was deployed as a reservoir engineer. The work in that niche suited him well. But not the bureaucracy. "I always liked to dig with a sharp shovel, as they say. I like to get things done." But getting things done, or at least getting things approved by management, was difficult. In one assignment, Jim had taken a bottom hole pressure measurement from a producing well. The project was simple enough, but he was made to rewrite his report several times because his writing style did not conform to the corporate template. He also devised a novel method of assessing an oil sample's *in situ* characteristics (that is, its chemical constitution while still in the reservoir, before being brought to the surface), but the powers that be were not open to novel, and they dismissed Jim's process. In such events, when his creativity and initiative were stymied by stodgy management, Jim generally responded in ways that did not help his cause—as he said, "I was not very good at company politics."

A friend from high school who had been best man in his wedding, Daroyl Curry, suggested to Jim that Skelly Oil in Tulsa allowed more freedom of motion. Daroyl made some introductions, and Jim was soon off to Tulsa.

He didn't go alone. Five years earlier, Jim had married Paula Hargrove, nine years his junior. Paula was born in Brownfield, Texas and raised in Carlsbad, New Mexico. She attended Midland Business College with two of her girlfriends from Carlsbad and, upon graduation, took a job with Phillips Petroleum as a geological technician (a *geotech* serves as a geologist's assistant). A true quick study, Paula loved the work and acquired a good knowledge of the geological side of the oil industry. She was grateful for the mentoring given her by the geologists she worked with, although she did not follow all of their advice: "One thing they taught me is that engineers are bad news, and they almost disinherited me when I married Jim." So goes the traditional cross-discipline rivalry.

Jim stayed at Skelly for almost five years, until Daroyl and his elder brother, Max, invited Jim to join them in Midland at their small-shop venture, Solar Oil Company. The organization had only ten employees, and Jim thought Solar might be the company he would end up running. He accepted their offer and joined them in early 1969 as chief engineer. He was thirty-five years old and one step from the completion of his plan.

Within six months of his arrival, the company folded. The company's financial backers went broke and took Solar down with them. Jim's Plan A was stalled, at least temporarily. He could find work at another small company and continue on, or regress to another major to wait for the next opportunity. Both options seemed doable, but neither was very exciting.

There was a third option: "Back in college I also had a Plan B: if I didn't like working for a company, I would start my own." Here was Jim's crossroads, and here was his decision to make: stay the Plan A course and throw in with another company, or switch to Plan B and go it on his own? Boring security or exciting risk?

By this time, there were family matters to be considered. Jim and Paula had their first two children in Tulsa, so when Solar closed its doors in Midland, the Henrys had little mouths to feed. Their situation was serious, but Paula, ever optimistic and firm in her faith, was not overly concerned: "As traumatic as it sounds, I wasn't that upset. Jim is brilliant—I knew he could get another job and so could I. We could live comfortably and that was all we cared about."

So, faced with Plan A versus Plan B, Jim completed his standard pro-and-con evaluation, then presented the lot to Paula: he could go to work for another company, small or large, or he could go out on his own. He was leaning toward the latter.

Paula's response, true to her character, was immediate: "Let's do it!"

Jim would be on his own, but not alone. Bob Landenberger, ten years Jim's senior, was chief geologist at Solar when the company folded. Like Jim, Bob had served in the Air Force and obtained a degree from OU, but Bob's degree was in geology. After bouncing between menial jobs at small oilfield vendors for a time, Bob hired on with Cities Service as a geologist and stayed with them for several years. He later left Cities and joined Yates Petroleum in Artesia, New Mexico for a few years before striking out on his own as a consultant. For reasons beyond his control, that venture had not gone well, but along the way he had done some work with the Curry brothers, who invited him to join Solar in mid-1968. When Jim showed up at Solar the next year, the two became good friends, admiring each other's technical abilities and work ethic.

But while Jim and Bob had a lot of background and character in common, their personalities were markedly different. As their longtime friend, Gene Sledge, put it, "What you're gonna have to learn about Jim is, there's not many funny stories. Jim was always serious, *always*—that's the engineer in him. Bob was a jokester. Those two guys were so opposite." Gene was good-naturedly exaggerating Jim's "serious" side, but he was leaning in the right direction. Bob's wife, Lynn, was a little understated in her assessment of the pair but said basically the same thing: "Bob and Jim were such good friends although they were so different—they complemented each other."

As a consequent outworking of their personalities, Jim and Bob looked at finances very differently. Jim was a planner, big on forecasts, budgets and balance sheets. Bob was happy-go-lucky, big on *que sera, sera*. During his consultant days, when he was barely getting by, Bob managed to land a gig that paid him $500. When he finished the job, he took his family on a $500 vacation and returned home broke again, although the family had collected some happy memories.

As Solar was winding down in late 1969, Lynn and Bob had six children, the oldest about to enter college and the youngest in kindergarten. "We had no money at all," Lynn said. So when Bob came home one day and said he had been talking with Jim, and told her, "We think we can do this on our own," her response to her husband was as affirmative as Paula's but, understandably, lacked the enthusiasm: "Well, Bob, if that's what you want to do, OK. We can't get any poorer than we are right now."

Lynn and Paula's relationship mirrored Bob and Jim's: "Paula was always so upbeat," Lynn said, "and I was just the opposite—I was the worrywart. Jim always gave me comfort because he always knew where every penny went." Paula's recollections expressed her reciprocal appreciation: "Bob Landenberger was a wonderful person and I knew that he and Jim would do well together." The pair presented the archetypal geologist-engineer antithesis: Bob was the *yang* to Jim's *yin*. And because of this, they stood an excellent chance of succeeding.

So it was decided. Jim, ever the planner, drew up a three-stage business strategy. They would begin as consultants. Consultants in the oil industry function much like those in other industries. They often do projects that are either too small or too large for a company to conduct with its own manpower, and they supply expertise that a company may lack. In the Permian Basin oil community, there are commonly small partnerships that have some, but not all, of the skills required for developing oil and gas prospects. For example, a lease negotiator might partner with a finance expert. The two together can handle the business, but not the technical aspects of geology and engineering. Such an entity might hire a Jim-and-Bob-type team to evaluate the potential of a lease, recommend drill sites and oversee the drilling of wells. Jim's plan was to provide all of these services in the first phase of their business.

Then, when they had established a proper reputation as skilled consultants, the partners would step up to *for-fee operators*. In petro parlance, an *operator*—specifically an *owner-operator*—is an entity that locates, drills for and produces oil and gas. (By the way, this segment of the petroleum industry is called the *upstream*.) Operators generally maintain a staff of people trained in all the skills requisite for the niche: geologists, engineers, field personnel, lease negotiators, legal eagles and finance folks. A large operator's staff may include several representatives of each discipline, while a small shop might have only one of each, or even fewer, with some of the employees wearing multiple hats. Most operators, whether large or small, outsource the actual drilling of wells to a drilling rig company, as a homeowner pays someone who owns a lawnmower to cut the grass. Operators also contract the *completion* work on their drilled wells. Completion is the process of stimulating and equipping a drilled well to enable it to produce from the downhole reservoir (this work includes *hydraulic fracturing*, which I will later describe in detail). But once the drilling and frac crews are done and dismissed, the operator maintains stewardship of the wells as they produce oil and gas. An operator's enterprise generally ends where the petroleum leaves the lease and is sold to the next link in the chain, as most operators (excepting mainly the largest, such as Exxon, Chevron and Shell) do not engage in transportation (trucking and pipelines), refining or marketing. (This segment is referred to as the *downstream*.)

All of that said, in Jim's second step of *for-fee operating*, they would conduct the leasing, planning, drilling and completion of the wells for the lease holder, who would assume responsibility for the wells once they have been brought *online* (that is, once they are actively producing oil and gas). So, a for-fee operator is akin to the building contractor who superintends the remodeling of your home, for a fee, and turns it over to you when the job is finished (not that a home remodeling job is ever finished). To augment their income from fees during this phase, Jim figured they would retain *overriding royalty interests*, or *overrides*, on the leases they secured for clients. An override in oil and gas is like a royalty in other enterprises: a share of the revenue from sales, without an accompanying share in the investment and expenses necessary to obtain it. Overrides of the type that the pair could keep are pretty small, and it takes a lot of them to generate significant cash flow. But every little bit would help.

Finally, with the money made from fees and overrides, Jim and Bob would transition to full-fledged, fully staffed owner-operators, as described above. They would hire a full staff to do their own prospecting and leasing, and they would keep a *working interest* in all the wells they drilled. A working interest, unlike a royalty interest, is burdened by the investment and expenses, but it can also be much larger and reap a greater share of the revenue and profit.

When they reached this point in the plan, the pair would be positioned to achieve Jim's ultimate goal of "self-sufficiency," which he defined as "not just having working interests, but enough of them such that the profits were sufficient to support our two families." Jim did not lay out a specific timeline for the parts of the plan, but he thought it would take about two years as consultants to become for-fee operators, maybe another two to begin drilling their own wells as owner-operators, and a few more to become self-sufficient.

As a first order of business, on November 1, 1969, the partners established an entity fittingly named for the initial phase of their plan: H&L Consultants. They set up shop at 2101 W. Texas Avenue in Midland, the former headquarters of Solar Oil, and used Solar's discarded office furniture to accouter it. They created a no-frills business card, including only their names and phone numbers and the address. And so, from a humble beginning, without any fanfare and certainly no indication of the great success that was to follow, the Henry oil company came into being.

Jim and Bob embarked on their venture without any money. "To say that we were insufficiently capitalized is an understatement," Jim remembered. "We had no money saved up. So we either got consulting work or we starved. And this was good because it made us more hungry." The pair did not want any financial backing; in fact, they were adamantly opposed to it. They were determined to maintain complete control of their business, and to reap all of its rewards. "We didn't want to get a money partner, because we didn't want to share our success with anybody."

But they did need money for office rent and overhead, not to mention food for their families, so they determined to take out a small loan. Not knowing any better, they went to a retail bank, Commercial Bank & Trust in downtown Midland. The officer was not sympathetic with their oil dream, but he agreed to grant them a $10,000 loan if Jim's father would cosign the note. James Henry was himself a small businessman who had done well as a farm equipment distributor, after leaving his earlier career as a mining engineer. He had counselled his son to avoid debt whenever possible: "I never saw a company go broke that didn't owe any money."

This advice became one of the earliest 'Jim-isms,' a set of guiding adages and proverbs that Jim continued to assemble and observe throughout his life. But debt-aversion notwithstanding, father and son saw the need for some credit, and the loan was duly secured.

Oil prices at the time were low, $3.35 per barrel. That's not quite as dismal as it sounds—the inflation-adjusted price is about $22 in today's dollars—but still, pretty dismal. Jim thought this might actually work on the partners' behalf. Low prices discouraged companies from hiring permanent employees, but there was ongoing work to be done, and perhaps companies would be more willing to hire temporary consultants. As Jim said, "We wouldn't have any problem finding consulting work." At least, that was his theory.

Jim was already doing some consulting with North American Royalties. In the early fall, when it was clear that Solar's end was near, the principals there allowed him to moonlight. The gig paid a total of $600. "Not much," Jim said, "but it helped us all through that first Christmas." Paula pitched into the effort and typed Jim's report at their breakfast table.

After the holidays, Bob got a call from Ernie Hanson, an independent oilman he had known in Artesia. Ernie offered Bob work as a geologist on two wells he was drilling near Tatum, New Mexico. Bob lived on location for six weeks, and Ernie paid him $125 a day. The money took care of both H&L families for a while, and shortly after Bob's stint ended, Jim scored again. He was walking east on Wall Street in downtown Midland one day, when he noticed Bob Bailey walking behind him. Bailey was a partner with Bailey, Sipes & Williamson Consulting Engineers, a well-connected local firm. Jim subtly slowed his pace so that Bailey would catch up with him. They talked as they walked together, and when they parted, Jim came away with more consulting work, at $10 an hour. Bailey saw value in Jim's master's degree "because," as Jim said, "he could tell his clients that the guy he was assigning to their job was worth his salt."

Ten dollars an hour does not a business make, especially with twelve mouths to feed, and H&L was still strapped. Suddenly, as Lynn describes it, "The tide began to turn. God has a plan, and lo and behold, Bob got another call from Ernie Hanson."

Ernie was wanting to expand his own oil business. He had been impressed with Bob's wellsite work, and by extension he trusted Jim. Ernie wanted H&L to help grow his footprint on the Midland side of the basin. He told Bob, "I'll set you and Jim up in an office, and I'll pay rent and utilities. You can buy office furniture, and I'll reimburse you. All I ask is, whatever you come up with [that is, drilling prospects], I want to see it first. If I don't want it, you can sell it to someone else." Hanson would pay them a finder's fee for every prospect they brought forward, with a bonus for those that Hanson chose to participate in. Hanson would also give H&L a small override in the leases they drilled, and would pay Jim and Bob daywork rates to oversee planning and drilling of the wells.

They inked the agreement on March 16, and, soon after, leased a new office, B105 in the Wall Towers West building. The *B* stood for basement level—wonderfully symbolic for the startup. On April 1, they hired their first employee, Doris Brooks, another Solar castoff who had been working for the pair part-time from the start. With their overhead largely provided, the opportunity for steady income and a full-time employee, H&L was moving on up.

———————

Three days after signing the agreement, H&L *spudded* (broke ground and began drilling) its first well for Hanson. The Atkins #1 was a *street deal*, a prospect generated by a local geologist, peddled to Jim and Bob for a fee and an overriding royalty. The location was in north-central Pecos County, where the strata are very shallow, and the primary target was the Ellenburger Formation at about 6200 feet. The team believed they had found a winner right out of the gate. But, as Jim recalled, "I learned something about the oil business in that first well: never get your hopes up too high."

They penetrated the target zone at the anticipated depth. It yielded good shows of gas while they were drilling through it, and the group excitedly prepared to run a *drill-stem test*. Called a *DST* for short, this test involves attaching a packer and a valve near the bottom of the drill pipe, lowering them into the hole and situating them so that oil and gas can flow up the pipe to the surface. The flowing rate and pressure are then used to determine whether the zone is worth completing.

But the DST didn't recover anything—the zone was a bust. "So at first it was 'yay!'" Jim said, "and we were jumping for joy, but then it was 'boo!'" As a last-chance effort to salvage the well, the team DST'd another zone, higher up in the wellbore. This test yielded gas at a rate of 675 MCFGD—not great, but plenty adequate to call for the completion crew. "So this time it was 'boo!' at first, but then 'yay!' We were up and down and up and down on this well." The Atkins #1 was completed flowing a respectable 983 MCFGD, a first feather in the partnership's cap.

Still in the spring of 1970, more work came H&L's way, this time in a project destined to reap rewards for more than a decade. As mentioned before, Jim had worked for Skelly Oil in Tulsa before joining the ill-fated Solar. He had maintained contact with his Skelly friends, and they knew he had set up his own consulting shop in Midland. Skelly's gas plant team hoped to profit from a growing collection of oil fields, known as the *Spraberry play*, then beginning to bloom in the Permian Basin. The Spraberry (pronounced SPRAY-berry) is an oil-productive *formation* (a rock layer or group of layers generally extending for hundreds or thousands of square miles) which the reader will hear much more about later. At the time, there were only about seventy Spraberry producers in Martin County, and Skelly wanted to determine whether the play would produce enough oil to justify building a processing plant.

They offered to pay H&L $7000 to evaluate the area's potential, so Jim and Bob set to work on the study while simultaneously servicing their Hanson agreement. "Bob and I worked on the study together. It took several months, and we did an excellent job of it, if I may say so myself."

Jim and Bob concluded that there would be hundreds of Spraberry wells in the future, but Skelly chose not to build a plant. By virtue of the contract, H&L was free to use the study findings for its own ends. "That gave us a start, because we became known as Spraberry experts. And people that wanted to drill in the Spraberry began to call us."

The partners now had paying overrides in several producing wells, a *résumé* of satisfied consulting customers, and a growing reputation as go-to Spraberry guys. Could things get much better? Well, yes, but not before they got much worse.

———————————

Tesoro Petroleum Corporation, headquartered in San Antonio, was primarily a refining company. They also engaged in oil exploration and production through *drilling fund partnerships*, publicly traded vehicles that provided a way for non-industry individuals to invest in oil and gas drilling ventures. The company initially retained H&L to work a few small consulting projects, but, in July 1970, while Bob and Jim were servicing their Hanson and Skelly agreements, a geological manager from Tesoro contacted them about a job on a much larger scale.

The man proposed that H&L serve as the general contractor for four Spraberry wells that would be part of a new drilling fund. Tesoro would pay H&L a fixed amount to *turnkey* each well. In a turnkey arrangement, the consultant drills the wells for an all-in fee, then turns the drilled wells over to the owner for completion and production. Jim and Bob could subcontract the actual drilling to a drilling rig company for a somewhat lesser amount, and keep the difference as profit, minus what they spent to get the location permitted and prepared. They figured they could make about $6000 profit on each of the wells, for a total of $24,000 (about $150,000 in today's dollars). And to cap off the deal, Tesoro wanted H&L to be the operators of record, which meant that they would be able to establish themselves as *bona fide* operators and no longer mere consultants.

Jim and Bob were ecstatic—this was the next step on their way to self-sufficiency, and they had reached it in less than a year. They were also amazed: the Skelly report had taken several months to complete, and earned them $7000; with Tesoro, they would make about that same amount of money for each well, with only a few days of work required for each one. It seemed too good to be true.

And so, of course, it was.

In the fall, the pair finished their existing projects and turned down all new jobs as they prepared for the Tesoro program. They identified a prospective *section* of land (one square mile, 640 acres), based on their Spraberry study, and acquired the leases with Tesoro funds. But in November, as the drilling time approached, the Tesoro man went silent. "He quit returning my calls," Jim said. "That was a very ominous sign." He finally heard back a few weeks before Christmas: "Sorry," the man said, "I couldn't raise the money." The fund was terminated, the deal was off, and H&L had nothing to fall back on. Jim was greatly discouraged. "We tried to get some more consulting work, and we started back up again. But it was scary—that was a very bleak Christmas."

In spite of its harsh end, H&L's first year was a moderate success. The partners had completed several consulting projects and were establishing a reputation for quality work and Spraberry savvy. They had their own digs, a full-time employee and much of their overhead covered. And when their twelve-month profit-and-loss statement was published, Jim and Bob found they'd made more money working for themselves than the previous year on salary with Solar.

———————————

The two went back to consulting in the first half of 1971, making calls and doing studies and generally "persevering," as Jim put it. And then in early summer, Good Providence called them higher.

Hanover Planning Company, Inc., like Tesoro, was an oil exploration and production company that raised money for its projects through drilling fund partnerships. But whereas Tesoro was based in Texas, Hanover was big league in the Big Apple—their front office was on Hanover Street in Lower Manhattan. Frank West, the company's president and COO, and his right-hand man, Gorman Webb, had heard about H&L's expertise in the Permian Basin Spraberry play, and contacted the pair in June.

Hanover (not to be confused with the aforementioned Hanson) was underway preparing for the 1971 edition of its annual $10 million drilling fund. Frank wanted H&L to identify and lease acreage north of Midland in Martin and Dawson Counties, based again on their knowledge of the play, and to prepare the locations and turnkey the drilling of Spraberry wells. His proposal included the same perk that Tesoro had offered: H&L would be the operator of record for the wells, rather than wellsite consultants. To top it off, Hanover's project was much larger than Tesoro's, and included eight sections of land. Frank structured his proposal such that H&L was first required to drill six Spraberry wells. If all went well, they had the option to drill another six, and finally another three. Jim and Bob accordingly dubbed the project "the 6-6-3 deal." The pair believed they would again clear a profit of about $6000 per well. They would use that margin to buy a 5% working interest in each well, and still have a little remaining to pay overhead. Here, then, was their do-over chance to move to the next phase of their business plan.

In early July, the Hanover deal was signed, the acreage acquired and well planning underway. But with oil at only $3.50 per barrel, Frank struggled to raise the necessary capital. For a moment it appeared that Hanover might go the way of Tesoro. Jim and Bob braced. But Frank determinedly searched for other investors to make the project happen. He called his friends Bertram Murphy and Lee Harvard, both of them oilmen in Roswell, New Mexico, and each with his own investor pool, and Hanover's offering was soon subscribed. "All of our dealings with Hanover were extremely pleasant. The fact that Frank honored his commitment to do something and found the investors was extremely important to our career." Frank's reliability and goodwill became a model for Jim in his own career: "The 6-6-3 deal ensured our success early on. And it only took place because we dealt with such honorable men as Frank West and Gorman Webb, who were trying to do not only what was good for them, but good for us also. We [the Henry oil company through the years] try to hold that same sort of ethic in everything that we do. We try to make sure that it's good for us *and* good for the people we're working with. And I was taught that by Frank West."

So, in July 1971, the partners were climbing from the second step in Jim's business plan to the third, just ahead of his back-of-the-envelope schedule. And because they were transitioning to owner-operators, they needed a new entity. They dissolved H&L Consultants, the first edition of the Henry oil company, and established a new and improved version in its place, Henry & Landenberger, Inc. Commensurate with their higher status, they created a spiffy corporate logo: a rock pick and slide rule, representing their dual geological-engineering skillset, with the slide rule positioned sideways atop the pick, such that the two together resembled a pumping unit. Jim and Bob included the logo on their new business cards, and the partnership was officially branded.

Because the pair had again dropped their consulting work, their new company would need an initial infusion of capital. And still they were determined not to have a backer: "We didn't want to be beholden to anybody. We didn't want someone to take 25% of all the hard work Bob and I were doing." They decided to take out another small loan, and went once again to Commercial Bank & Trust. The loan officer again required a cosigner, but now the partners had built up overrides worth about $25,000 and they offered these as collateral. The officer, still uncomfortable with oil ventures, said he would talk to the loan committee.

When two months passed without a response, the pair approached First National Bank, which was more of an "oil bank," where the officers understood the petroleum world. There they met with VP Wilbur Yeager. Jim recalled that Wilbur, with no fuss whatsoever, pulled out of his right-hand desk drawer a one-page contract and simply asked, "How much do you need?" Jim told him $20,000, and the loan was approved. First National was the partners' go-to lender from that point forward.

Jim had another recollection of that meeting: "I remember how nervous Bob was when we went in to see Wilbur. His hands were shaking." I asked why, and Jim winced and shook his head, "Bob had bad experience with banks." Of course he did.

August 8, 1971, is an historic date in the Henry oil company annals. On that day, to kick off the Hanover Planning 6-6-3 project, Henry & Landenberger spudded its first well as operator of record. The Yates #1, located near the Sulfur Draw Field in Dawson County, was headed for the Dean Formation at a planned total depth (*TD*) of 9300 feet.

It didn't quite make it. Something went wrong at 4084 feet,

not quite halfway down. The records are scant, and the final entry on the drilling report reads: "LOST FISH AND COULD NOT RECOVER." (*Fish* is the term for drilling pipe and equipment broken off in a wellbore.) The well was plugged and abandoned—not an auspicious beginning, but, to put it optimistically, the sort of training project that a shiny new oil company needs to welcome it to the big-boy world of operating.

Undaunted, Jim and Bob quickly permitted and spudded a second well on the same location, the Yates #1Y (the *Y* signifying a replacement well). This one went down without issue, and on October 20, 1971, Henry & Landenberger completed its first producing well, flowing from the Dean at an impressive rate of 135 BOPD.

The Henry oil company was on the scoreboard.

Chapter 2
A Little Ol' Spraberry Driller

HENRY & LANDENBERGER drilled on. They completed about two wells per month in late 1971, with $6000 profit ringing the cash register each time. "We started making real money then," Jim said. "It had taken several months as consultants for us to make the amount we could make on a single well. It's what gave us our start. It made the company at that time." Jim deeply appreciated the Hanover team for their tangible vote of confidence, and he was particularly grateful to Frank West, who made the deal work not only for himself, but for all the parties involved.

Several other men helped Jim and Bob during their formative years as Spraberry operators, and their names likewise appear on Jim's gratitude list. John Cox, who was known as "Mr. Spraberry," is near the top. John established his own reputation as an oilman by figuring out how to drill Spraberry wells cheaply. Since its start in the 1950s, the Spraberry was considered a "cost play," meaning that the formation had a very narrow profit margin—the costs of drilling were high relative to its productivity—and operators could only make money if they drilled very efficiently. John could be "kind of a forceful personality," Jim said, but he gave his time and guidance freely. "I often went to him for advice. He always spent time with me, wouldn't just shove me aside. He was a good man and he helped me a lot, and everyone looked up to him like I did."

Successful Spraberry players Howard Parker and Joe Parsley are also on Jim's list. While Parker & Parsley conducted much of its business through drilling funds, the principals advised Jim not to get into that practice. He took that advice, and although he often drilled and operated wells for drilling fund managers, he never created a fund of his own.

Jim especially appreciated the mentoring of Jack Major. The Major, Geibel and Forrester Partnership was one of Midland's most successful independent drillers back in the day. Yet even in their high-rise success, "Jack [Major] went out of his way to help get me started. He was so nice and helped me wherever he could."

Like the other "big boys" Jim sought out, Tom Brown, founder of Tom Brown Drilling, was very successful by that time. "He was a step higher than me—it's like I was in high school and he was in college." Although Jim didn't know him well, "he was always very helpful, and I appreciated that."

These men, and others, helped Jim become not merely a better driller but a better man, and he has tried always to pay the blessing forward: "I tell you these names because they meant a lot to me. When someone is starting out, I feel for them, because I know how I felt, and I want to help like the people that were so helpful to me."

By late 1971, after four months as operators, Henry & Landenberger had drilled seven wells. They spudded the eighth, the Parham #1, on November 26, in north-central Martin County. The well was being drilled for Hanover Planning, but it was not included in the 6-6-3 project. Frank West had acquired some additional acreage that he held back for Hanover and a few other investors, and the Parham was part of that program. Consequently, Jim and Bob did not own a working interest in the well, but they did have a small override that Frank had given them as a reward for their excellent work.

Like the previous wells, this one was headed for the Spraberry Formation. But the group wanted to test a shallow zone along the way. Jim and Bob had learned that some of the existing Spraberry wells in this vicinity had encountered excellent oil shows while drilling in the Grayburg Formation, at about 4000 feet. So the team designed the Parham well to stop at the Grayburg and run a DST (remember, *drill-stem test*) before drilling on to the Spraberry.

But something went wrong during the test. The Grayburg was unexpectedly over-pressured, which caused the downhole packer to fail. Oil began flowing around the packer and up into the space between the drill pipe and the borehole wall, where it was very difficult to contain. The crew tried for several hours to prevent the oil from reaching the surface by pumping heavy mud into the well, but to no avail. By next morning, the pressure of the flow had increased to a threatening level, and the rig owner decided to close the special valve at the top of the wellhead (appropriately called a *blowout preventer*, or BOP) and figure out another plan of attack. But the valve was rusted from disuse—Spraberry drilling was not normally this exciting—and the crew was unable to screw it shut.

A stream of highly flammable oil and gas now began spewing from the wellhead. As the crew darted away, the jetting oil reached one of the derrick lights, which shattered and ignited the stream. The explosion did not topple the derrick but knocked it to one side. Oil continued to rocket out of the hole, combusting as soon as it reached the surface like a giant flamethrower extending 40 feet into the sky. By grace, the crew all made it to safety, and no one was injured.

The rig owner, who by virtue of the turnkey arrangement was

responsible for the well, called Halliburton (an oilfield service company) and they came quickly to the scene. Jim and Bob were also summoned but could do no more than gaze from a distance at the gargantuan ball of fire hovering above the listing derrick. After many hours, the flow subsided enough that the crew could construct a makeshift flowline and resume pumping heavy mud down the hole. They were able finally to kill the flow and quench the flame, but by this time the drilling rig had melted down and was welded into a twisted mass.

The cottonfield around the location was badly damaged. But Mr. Parham—who owned both the surface and the subsurface, the cotton and the oil—was kindly forbearing and chose not to litigate, as some landowners would surely have done. He asked only for the cleanup and remediation expenses, which he received. Of course, as the mineral owner, Mr. Parham did get an excellent mailbox job from the ensuing production. After the burned-up rig carcass was removed, the crew was able to complete the well, and on March 11, 1972, four months after it spudded, the Parham #1 was flowing oil and gas from the Grayburg at 400 BOEPD. Co-investor Bert Murphy, a man of letters, drew from his knowledge of Egyptian mythology to choose a fitting name for the new field: Phoenix.

Henry & Landenberger fulfilled their 6-6-3 project with Hanover in mid-1972. As a result of the Parham discovery, Frank West had pivoted away from his Spraberry plan and swapped some Phoenix Grayburg wells into the remaining drilling schedule. Jim and Bob were consequently able to acquire an early working interest in the field, which in the future would resurrect more than once to bless the Henry oil company.

Now, with their Hanover obligations fulfilled and profits realized, the pair began developing home-grown Spraberry prospects, still using their Skelly study as a guide. They were firmly on the third step in Jim's business plan and headed for self-sufficiency. "We would work up a prospect and buy the leases and then get partners to drill with us," Jim said. "There were hundreds of locations to be had."

To facilitate their growing business as owner-operators, Jim and Bob created a partner investment structure that would serve the company for more than twenty years. In their template, the investor group paid Henry & Landenberger a capital fee of 7% of the drillwell cost estimate (called the *authority for expenditure*, or AFE). The pair also received a 7% *carried* interest in each well. That is, the investors collectively paid for 100% of the well in return for a 93% interest, with Jim and Bob keeping the rest. And they used a portion of their 7% capital fee to purchase an additional 5% working interest in every well. When all the math was done, Henry & Landenberger had a 12% working interest in each well (7% carried plus 5% pay-their-way) and 2% of the AFE left over to pay their overhead. They dubbed the structure "the 7 and 7," which over time earned for itself a prefix of distinction: 'the *Ol'* 7 and 7.'

As a result of their success with Hanover, Henry & Landenberger attracted an early and continuing group of investors, among them Bert Murphy (who named the Phoenix) and Lee Harvard, both from the original Hanover deal. Jim's friend and local businessman Joe Henderson, who owned a local drilling mud company, took 5% in everything Henry & Landenberger did. The pair also picked up some much deeper pockets from the northeast, including the New York Life Insurance Company and the Yale Endowment.

Jim and Bob also found another investor unintentionally, a man who became a close friend. The Nail #1 well, located in the Fran-Glass Field of Martin County, was the first well that Henry & Landenberger contracted with rig company Chaparral Drilling. Gene Sledge had recently become a partner in Chaparral, but he had never before been on a drilling rig. "I was never a *roughneck* [a rig worker] and I was never on a rig floor," he said, "I was always in sales or management. The Nail was my first venture into drilling."

Unlike most wells that Jim and Bob had drilled to this point, the Nail would be drilled to the Strawn Formation, a zone far below the Spraberry, at a depth of 10,600 feet. The well's primary target was still the Spraberry, but as the Strawn was also productive in the vicinity, the investors agreed that drilling deeper was worth a shot. So they ponied up the cost to drill an additional 1200 feet.

The Spraberry, Dean and Wolfcamp were drilled without issue, but as soon as they penetrated the Strawn it began *kicking* (flowing high-pressured oil into the wellbore). As Chaparral was drilling the well for Jim and Bob on a turnkey contract, it was up to Gene to figure out how to handle the problem. He quickly ordered some high-dollar heavy drilling mud brought to the location, and each time it kicked, the crew pumped more of it down the hole to try to force the flow back into the formation. "The mud man took me aside, up on the rig floor, and said, 'Gene, you need to get out of this, pal. The mud bill will be more than your contract.'" Gene was in a conundrum: "I had just joined Chaparral as an owner, and this was my first well, and I was thinking, 'What the hell did I do?'"

In the end, Gene and crew were able to get control of the well and finish drilling it. The Nail was then completed on December 1, flowing 130 BOPD. Gene honored his contract in spite of the expensive mud bill. Jim was impressed that, though Gene was an owner in the rig company, he had come personally to the wellsite and stayed through the end of the ordeal. "Gene lived up to his word. He was always such a good drilling contractor. We never had any problems with him. His work was always well done. Gene was the best."

Two years later, Gene left Chaparral and formed his own rig company, Gene Sledge Drilling. He did almost all of Henry & Landenberger's drilling for the next several years, and took a 6%

working interest in every well. Jim, Bob and Gene became good friends, professionally and personally. Jim and Gene were still having lunch once a month fifty years later, ending only when Gene passed away in 2020.

———————

As a result of their growing well count, Henry & Landenberger needed a higher headcount. In July 1971, as the 6-6-3 project was getting underway, Jim hired E. M. "Red" Daugherty to work in the office as a liaison with all the projects in the field. Red had just retired from Amerada Hess Corporation and wanted to keep working a while longer, but for a smaller shop. Soon afterward, they hired Carolyn Minnerly (who, for reasons no one can remember, went by the nickname "Pete") to be their full-time bookkeeper. While Jim was big on keeping records, he knew little about accounting rules, and sometimes his method for reporting financial details was unintentionally improper. "Don't short-leg it, Jim!" Pete would admonish him. "Do it right!"

The company also needed some eyes in the field and boots on the ground to supervise drilling and production, and Red Dougherty knew the perfect man for the job. He had worked with Harold Meredith at Amerada for many years. Like Red, Harold had recently retired but was not quite ready for the rocking chair. Jim hired him in October 1972, when Harold was 59. "I can give you two or three more years," he told Jim. Jim replied, "Harold, you've got a good twenty left."

It turned out to be thirty.

———————

In 1972, Jim and Bob's first full year as operators, they drilled nineteen wells, and in the following year, twenty-two. Late that year, along with the rest of US oil operators, the pair got a huge boost from international politics. In response to US support of

Israel in the Arab-Israeli War, Arab OPEC members imposed an oil embargo on the US and other supportive countries. Oil shot up from $4.30 per barrel in the fall of 1973 to $10.11 in January 1974 (from $28 to $64 in today's dollars). And so, with this financial tailwind, Henry & Landenberger drilled ahead.

They spudded their first well of the new year on January 6, in Martin County on a small farm owned by one Roy Tidwell. Tidwell had retired and bought 160 acres to farm as a hobby, but his retirement had not gone as planned. He was on the brink of losing the place when Henry leased his farm and drilled a well. The royalty stream paid off Tidwell's loan and allowed him to keep the land. Johnny Brown, Henry's long-time lease operator, maintained the well for much of its life. He recalled that "every year, Tidwell planted eight rows a half-mile long, with corn, okra, watermelon, cantaloupes, squash. He'd mix them up in his planter boxes and plant them up and down the side of the county road for us—he called them 'the Henry rows.' He said, 'That's for you Henry guys. Whatever you want out of it, take it,' because Henry had saved his farm and treated him so well."

And the well was a gift that kept on giving to the Tidwell family. It has the second highest cumulative production of all Henry & Landenberger wells, having made 240 MBO in its 46-year life before being plugged in late 2020. That's almost biblical, lacking only the widow and her jar.

The specifics of the Tidwell story are unique, but the tale manifests a common theme of goodwill between the Henry company and its lessors. Johnny remembered that "most of the farmers in Martin and Dawson County, for years, would tell each other, 'If you're going to lease your land, get Henry to do it, because Henry'll take care of it.'"

———————

Henry & Landenberger continued to grow in size and reputation, and by Jim's reckoning the partners achieved their goal of self-sufficiency in mid-1974, well ahead of schedule. In April of the next year, the partners vacated their basement office and moved into the Petroleum Building, suite 810—no *B* this time. They were moving up.

Jim and Bob were by now operating more than fifty wells, but their success was not apparent to everyone, even on the inside. One day, Lynn Landenberger and her friend, Marcie Christensen, were sitting in Marcie's car in a junior high parking lot, waiting for their girls to finish band practice. Their friend, a local oilman, walked up to the car on Marcie's side. After exchanging greetings, he said, "You know your husband's really doing well in the business," and he began to talk about oil and drilling. Lynn's mind wandered: "I thought he was talking to Marcie because Max [Marcie's husband] was already well established. And I was just kind of looking around. And then it got real quiet. And then I turned around and said, 'Oh, are you talking to *me*?' And he said, 'Yes, I am.' I said, 'Oh, that's news to me, because I won't think we're doing well until I see new carpet in our den!'"

The partners needed more help in the field to service their ever-increasing well inventory. In March 1976, they hired JC "Pete" Peterson to serve as a foreman under Harold, and signed two contract pumpers later that year: Dick Madison, the first of three Madison generations to work for Henry, and the aforementioned Johnny Brown, who had just finished serving in the Air Force. And because more wells means more leases, they brought on Cliff Hair as the company's in-house expert on land affairs. These hirings raised Henry & Landenberger's full-time roster to eight, plus a handful of contract field hands.

Then in early 1977, with everything moving in the right direction, Bob abruptly decided to call it quits. He was in his mid-50s. Four of his children were in college, and he felt he had already missed out on a lot of their lives because of the rigorous six-day work week he and Jim had observed since starting the company. Lynn did not want her husband to retire yet. "Why," she asked him, "when we're doing so well?" But she understood. Bob had entered the military as soon as he graduated from high school and gone immediately overseas for three years, from 1942 to 1945, during World War II. He enrolled in college as soon as he got out, and he and Lynn got married two years before they graduated. "He just really didn't get a chance to enjoy life and our children until he retired."

Jim, then 45, likewise understood Bob's desire. "But his leaving was very difficult on me, because he was such a great partner—he kept me stabilized and was someone I could turn to when things got very tough." In particular, Jim recalled an exchange they frequently had while discussing opportunities that Jim felt were essential to the company's wellbeing. "I would be saying, 'Bob, we've *got* to do this, we *have* to do this!' And he would say, 'No, Jim, we don't *have* to do it.' There would always be another good deal out there. He kept me grounded."

Bob took his share of the business primarily in properties. The partners evenly split the overrides and working interests, and Jim paid Bob for the office furniture and gave him some cash besides. By all accounts, Bob's decision to retire was premature, especially given his financial habits. But he continued to dabble in oil and gas and sometimes brought prospects to Jim. Eventually the money got tight, and out of gratitude for his role in helping the families become successful, Jim and Paula established a retainer for him. Bob did some on-and-off work during the next few years until he became disabled. Even then, Jim and Paula continued the retainer, and after Bob passed away in 2012, they increased it, despite Lynn's protests. "They were so very generous. But I finally asked them to stop, and they did. My children are all wonderful to me. I have a good life, and I don't need to worry about money anymore."

Lynn also held onto Bob's overrides, as he had instructed her, and she recently began receiving revenue from a lease drilled horizontally by Diamondback Energy. "So at age 92," she said, "I guess I'm still an oil woman!"

———————————

Henry & Landenberger spudded its final well, the Brown #1, on April 23, a few weeks after Bob left. The well, located in the Phoenix Field, was a dry hole.

During its six-year life, the Henry & Landenberger partnership had drilled a total of eighty-nine wells, most within the area Jim and Bob originally outlined in their Skelly project: fifty-one in Martin and seventeen in Dawson. The rest were sprinkled across Midland, Upton, Reagan and Andrews. Combined, Henry & Landenberger's wells ultimately produced just under 5 MMBO and 9 BCFG. Although it began with a junked hole, this second version of the Henry oil company had ultimately achieved success and established self-sufficiency for the partners.

Jim and Paula created the third edition of their oil company, Henry Petroleum Corporation, when Henry & Landenberger was dissolved in early 1977. Jim retained the pick-and-rule icon on his new business cards, but he moved the office to suite 801, a few paces down the hall, to accommodate his growing employee count. After taking a few months to get the dissolution squared away and the new company up and running, Henry Petroleum spudded its inaugural well on September 2. The Smith #1 was permitted and drilled as a Spraberry-Dean test in the Tex-Hamon Field in Dawson County. The well sputtered at best, and was plugged and abandoned less than two years later. As with the previous Henry version, this was not a great beginning. Yet Henry & Landenberger had ended well. And Henry Petroleum would end spectacularly.

The path to that spectacle would require Henry to grow and mature, to become more sophisticated in all aspects of its projects and arrangements—low-margin, same-ol' Spraberry programs could build the company only so big.

Readers not fluent in geo-speak may already be wondering, "What exactly is a basin? What's a Wolfcamp, and what's an oil reservoir"? And from this point in the story, as the company begins to take on new ventures, the tale will present more geo-vocabulary. So it may be helpful now to pull over for a chapter, and learn a little more about the Permian Basin and its geology.

Chapter 3
Permian Basin Rocks for Jocks

EVERY INDUSTRY HAS its own language, a vocabulary and grammar that insiders use to describe its essential and distinctive concepts. Petroleum's language, as you have seen, is rooted in geologic and engineering concepts, many of which are unfamiliar to readers outside (and even many inside) the business. Later in the story, when Henry reaches the Wolfberry epic, we will explore hydraulic fracturing, which is primarily an engineering concept particularly pertinent to those events. For now, the reader may need a basic survey of Permian Basin geology, which underlies all of Henry's history.

The Permian Basin

So what is *Permian*?

Well, yes, it is a high school in Odessa that was the setting for *Friday Night Lights*. But the name goes back a lot farther than the school. The Permian is a geologic period in earth history, reckoned by contemporary geoscientists to span from 300 to 250 million years ago. The *type locality* for the Permian period is the region around the city of Perm in west-central Russia. (A type locality is the location where rock strata occur that are regarded as defining the characteristics typical of a particular geological age or formation.) Much of the oil produced in West Texas and southeastern New Mexico comes from Permian-age strata, hence the name of the basin. (And in case you're wondering, while Odessa, Texas was also named after a city in Eurasia, that city is in Ukraine, about 1800 miles west of Perm. There is no link between the names of Odessa and the Permian Basin. Except for the high school.)

So that explains Permian. But why do we call it a *basin*? There certainly is no ocean basin to be seen here today.

True. The present-day topography is pretty much flat as a pancake—the town of Levelland, two hours north of Midland, is aptly named. That said, the area *does* bear at least a superficial resemblance to a beach: flat, sandy and hot. We locals like to say that Midland is on the beach, it's just a long way from the water. But there actually is a basin here, only not at the surface. Our basin is buried deep in the subsurface. It turns out that during the Permian age in geologic history, West Texas was not *near* the water, it was *under*water.

Structural Geology of the Permian Basin

To be accurate, the Permian Basin proper is not a single basin but two basins situated side by side, with a partition between them. The *Midland Basin*, on the east, is about 100 miles wide and 200 miles long. It extends southeasterly from Terry and Lynn counties in the north to Crockett and Schleicher in the south. And to the west, the *Delaware Basin* is somewhat triangular and reaches from Eddie and Lea counties in New Mexico, southward for about 150 miles to almost the center of Pecos County, Texas.

The two basins are separated by an uplifted geologic feature about 50 miles wide that trends along the same southeasterly azimuth. This feature is called the *Central Basin Platform* (CBP), and it presents something like a dividing wall. During Permian time, water over the platform ranged from maybe ten to a hundred feet deep, while the Midland Basin was a few thousand feet at its deepest, and the Delaware a few thousand more than that. Each of the basins is asymmetrical in depth, like a swimming pool with a shallow end and a deep end. The shallow end of the Midland Basin is along its eastern margin, or *shelf*. From its shelf, the basin floor slopes downward to the west, deeper and deeper, until it meets the platform, where it rises abruptly as if it were hitting a wall. The Delaware Basin is basically its mirror image, with its shallow end along its western margin, and its deep end in the east, where it abuts the base of the platform. All tallied and with its peripheral noses, arches and shelves, the entire Permian Basin covers 86,000 square miles.

Sedimentology of the Permian Basin

The Midland and Delaware basins are not visible at the surface today because they were gradually filled in with sediment by natural processes, and this sediment became both the source and the container of the oil and gas that we're talking about. There are primarily two types of *sedimentation* (also called *deposition*) which between them generate the three rock types essential to the basin's petroleum cache: *sandstone*, *limestone*, and the globally hot topic of today's oil conversation, *shale*.

Clastic Deposition

Clastic deposition is a pretty straightforward process: existing rock strata exposed at the earth's surface are eroded by water and weather, and the resulting broken pieces, or *clasts* (also called *detritus*), are carried away by wind, rivers and streams, and deposited in lakes and oceans. Over time the sediments are buried under more sediment and, with increasing temperature and pressure and chemical activity, they become *lithified*, from the Greek word *lithos* for rock.

The rock type formed by lithification of clastic deposits is called *sandstone*. Sandstone formations in the Permian Basin have yielded tremendous reserves through the years—much of the Spraberry Formation is composed of sandstone, as is the Grayburg at the Phoenix Field. But, to be technically accurate, *sand* doesn't refer to what the clasts are *composed of*, but to their *size*. Sandstone describes rocks composed of clasts between 0.1 and 1.0 millimeters in diameter—the size of the stuff between your toes at Galveston (or in your mouth at Monahans). Successively finer detritus is termed *silt* and *clay*, and rocks composed of these clastic types are named *siltstone* and *claystone*. Going the other way, detritus coarser than sand includes *pebbles*, *cobbles* and *boulders*, and rocks composed of these larger clast sizes are collectively called *conglomerates*.

Carbonate Deposition

Most of the sedimentation in both the Midland and Delaware basins during the Permian period was clastic. But up on the platform, a very different process was taking place, called *carbonate deposition*.

During the geologic time straddling the Permian, most of the earth's continental crust, riding atop tectonic plates, was jammed together in a colossal landmass known as *Pangaea*. The name is from the Greek words *pan*, meaning all or whole, and *gaia*, from the root word for earth—hence *Pangaea*, All Earth.

The part of Pangaea that is now West Texas was situated on or about the equator. Then, as now, the water temperature, clarity and acidity of shallow equatorial seas were optimal for the biochemical precipitation of *calcium carbonate*, also known by its mineral name, *calcite*. Calcite is formed when microscopic organisms, such as bacteria, induce chemical precipitation by excreting their waste. A vast cast of sea critters, ranging from plankton and red algae to corals, clams, starfish and oysters, harvest that calcite, and use it to construct their shells. When these critters die, their shells are broken up by currents and waves, and form beautiful white sand beaches and underwater shoals.

Rock types formed by the lithification of these sediments of broken shells are collectively called *carbonates*, the most common of which is *limestone*. The thick layers of fossil-rich limestone atop the Central Basin Platform are the evidence by which we conclude that West Texas was situated near the equator during Permian time, in a setting similar to the present-day Bahamas. (And we further conclude that the Permian version of West Texas was much prettier than the present one.)

Because carbonate deposition is limited to relatively shallow water depths, carbonates in the Permian Basin formed primarily on the platform and around the basin rim, or *shelf*. Prolific oil reservoirs such as the Wolfcamp, Clearfork and San Andres formations (listed oldest to youngest) are examples of such deposits. During the time of the Wolfcamp deposition, the carbonate sediments accumulating near the edge of the platform and rim grew thicker, taller and more precarious, until periodic violent storms and shifting ocean currents destabilized the deposits and sent them cascading down the sides and into the basin. The resulting carbonate detritus piled up in heaps at the bottom of the slope and in submarine deltas extending out a few miles. The result was a miles-wide band of detrital carbonate sediment that runs along the basin floor, parallel to the platform edge, mixed with the fine-grained clastic deposits that more routinely settled there.

Clear as mud? This all may sound needlessly technical. But it so happens that this band of detrital limestone mixed with clastic deposits in the Wolfcamp Formation made Jim and Paula a lot of money, and enabled them to wonderfully bless everybody around them. Stay tuned.

The Special Case of Shale

Shale is a special type of clastic sedimentary rock that plays a critical role in the petroleum industry, and warrants a bit more say. A true shale, in the technical sense, is clastic rock formed from a mixture of the two finest detritus types, silt and clay. Detritus this fine can easily be carried along by even slow-moving currents, whether in streams or oceans—think of the muddy Mississippi River. Only where the waters are very calm, such as far offshore and below wave base, do the clay and silt fall out of suspension and settle on the basin floor, where they become lithified into the rock type called shale.

But shale often has an additional and very important ingredient. The earth's oceans are literally cloudy with *plankton*, a collective term that includes all manner of micro critters from algae, bacteria and ciliates to fungi and forams and flagellates. Plankton have no means of locomotion; they are simply carried along by whatever current is present. When they die, their organic matter joins the steady underwater rain of inorganic silt and clay blanketing the sea floor and becomes lithified along with them. As the shale is buried deeper and subjected to greater temperatures, the organic matter breaks down into *hydrocarbons*, that is, oil and gas. Shales composed of at least one-half percent of *total organic carbon* (TOC) by weight are referred to as *source rocks* because they are a source—in fact, far and away the *major* source—of the earth's hydrocarbons. Globally, shale source rocks average about 2% TOC. In the Permian Basin, shale strata contained in both the Wolfcamp and Spraberry Formations (among others) have TOCs in this range. Some shales have much higher TOCs. For example, the Bakken Formation in North Dakota and Montana, the Marcellus Shale in

Appalachia, and the Woodford Shale in Texas and Oklahoma all have 15–20% TOC in places.

Much of the hydrocarbon generated within shale migrates out of its parent rock via faults and natural fractures, and winds up trapped in porous sandstone and limestone reservoirs (more on this below). But shales that retain a significant amount of oil and gas, such as those named above, are reservoirs themselves. These self-sourced shale reservoirs are the target of the contemporary and much-ballyhooed *horizontal shale play*. (In the petroleum industry, a play is a reservoir, or collection of reservoirs, with a set of distinctive characteristics in common, such as geologic setting, rock type, or trapping mechanism.) There will be much more about horizontal shale drilling later in the book.

Summary of Permian Deposition

During earliest Permian time, carbonates were being prolifically manufactured in the shallow waters atop the Central Basin Platform and around the basin rim. In the Midland Basin, fine-grained clastics (silt and clay) were being continually delivered by rivers and streams to the gently sloping eastern perimeter, and slowly filling in the basin from east to west. Meanwhile, all along the basin's western margin, where it meets the platform, heaps of limestone detritus, ranging from fine-grained silt to huge boulders and blocks, were episodically being slumped, dumped and poured into the basin, as described above. The result was a five-to-ten-mile-wide band around the bottom, within which layers of coarse limestone detritus alternate irregularly with layers of shale. Similar processes were mirrored in the Delaware Basin, on the west side of the platform. The package of rock resulting from these processes during early Permian time is named the *Wolfcamp Formation* in both basins and on the platform.

As the Permian progressed, after the time of Wolfcamp deposition, the influx of clastics from the east into the Midland Basin increased, and coarser clastics (sand along with silt and clay) dominated the sediment profile. The resulting rock package from this time is named the *Spraberry Formation*. Again, similar processes were mirrored in the Delaware Basin, where the package has a different name, the *Bone Spring Formation*. Carbonate shoals and reefs continued to form on the platform, where the resulting formations of this time are called the *Wichita* and *Clearfork Formations*.

Eventually, the Midland Basin was all but filled in by clastic deposits, and the water was shallow over the whole expanse. The carbonate deposition that had been limited to the platform and rim was now able to spread out across most of the basin, and the resulting carbonate deposits are named the *San Andres Formation*. In the Delaware Basin, however, which was deeper than the Midland and not so easily filled in, clastic deposition continued, and the resulting thick succession of sandstones is collectively called the *Delaware Sands*.

Porosity and Permeability

Now that we've established a working knowledge of large-scale geologic structures, processes and formations, we need to zoom in to some important smaller-scale characteristics of the rocks themselves.

Porosity

Most sedimentary rock is not really solid but is riddled with holes, and these holes collectively constitute the rock's *porosity*. Porosity is simply the amount of void space (or *pore* space) in a rock layer, and it is expressed as a percentage of the total rock volume.

The pore spaces of a rock layer contain some mixture of oil, gas and water. Water is the predominant fluid in porosity, because most sediments were deposited in water, and groundwater pervades the earth's crust. But because hydrocarbon is less dense than water, as oil and gas percolate from shale source rocks upward into overlying strata, they displace much of the resident water. When we refer to a rock layer as an oil or gas *reservoir*, we mean that its pores contain a significant amount of hydrocarbon, which can be extracted from the rock by drilling wells into it.

In clastic sedimentary rocks, the most common type of porosity is formed by the spaces between the clasts or grains, called *intergranular porosity*. It may surprise you that spaces so tiny as those between sand grains would even be worth considering, but a simple experiment will demonstrate their importance: fill a plastic bottle with dry clean sand, all the way to the brim. Now slowly pour water into the bottle, and you will see that you can add quite a bit, likely about a third of the volume of the empty bottle. The porosity in sedimentary clastics ranges from near zero up to 20–25%, and it is determined largely by the *sphericity* (roundness) and *sorting* (the range of sizes) of the grains, as well as the *degree of cementation* (that is, the extent to which chemically precipitated minerals have filled the pores).

Carbonate sedimentary rocks may also have intergranular porosity, and other types as well. The fossilized shells that make up the rock are often hollow, for example gastropods (snails) and bivalves (clams and mollusks), and these hollows are sometimes preserved as porosity. And calcite—the mineral that makes up limestone—dissolves easily in subsurface waters, leaving voids of various shapes and sizes. When these dissolution voids are tiny, we call them *vugs* or *molds*, and when they are very large, we call them Carlsbad Caverns.

Permeability

Whereas porosity is a measure of how much of a rock layer is composed of void spaces, *permeability* is a measure of how easily fluids can move between those spaces. The basic unit of measurement for permeability is the *darcy*, named after the French engineer, Henry Darcy, who pioneered permeability studies.

Permeability is largely determined by two factors: how well the pore spaces are connected to each other, and the sizes of the pore *throats* connecting them. Imagine a gymnasium filled completely with basketballs from floor to ceiling. This simulates a sedimentary rock layer composed of very large clasts. The room has excellent porosity, as there are spaces between all the balls. The pores are also wonderfully connected—you could easily snake a hose through the balls from one end of the gym to the other. Because the throats between the spaces are also very large, this simulated layer has both high porosity and high permeability: it will hold a great amount of fluid, and it will transmit the fluid quite easily and at a fast rate. The porosity of this setup is about 35%, and the permeability is a million or more darcys.

Now remove the basketballs, and imagine the same gym filled with BBs to represent a layer composed of much smaller clasts. Because porosity is not impacted by grain size, this layer has exactly the same porosity as the basketball layer, about 35%. Again the pores are well connected—spheres are spheres, whether large or small, and the pore spaces and throats between them are exactly the same shapes and *relative* proportions. But unlike the previous case, the *absolute size* of these pore throats is tiny, and fluids will have a tougher time flowing through a gym filled with BBs than one full of basketballs. So this scenario has high porosity, but low permeability. That said, the permeability of a roomful of BBs is still excellent by natural oil reservoir standards, in the range of a few hundred darcys.

In nature, there are no strata made of perfectly round, perfectly sorted grains like BBs and basketballs (although a few come close). Real-life sandstone reservoirs have permeabilities in the range of a few tens to even a few hundreds of *millidarcys* (a millidarcy is one

one-thousandth of a darcy) owing to poor sorting, angular grains and pore-filling minerals. The permeability of clastic siltstones and shales, which are much finer-grained, is thousandths to hundredths of a millidarcy. We describe such low-perm rock as *tight*, most often spelled *tite*. The porosity and permeability of carbonate reservoirs are highly variable.

Finally, open natural fractures in rock strata also increase permeability by providing a more efficient pathway for transmitting fluids. Later in the story, we will consider the very important practice of artificially inducing fractures in low-permeability rocks to improve their permeability.

To close out this geology course, I will synthesize all this information to tell the story of the two contemporary rock stars of the Permian Basin.

In 1917, a team of three geologists from the University of Texas's Bureau of Economic Geology conducted a survey of the Glass Mountains in southern West Texas. They were led by Johan Udden, a Swedish chap who had recently been installed as the bureau's first director. At one field site, the trio found a 500-foot-thick outcrop of black and gray shale, with alternating layers of limestone, which they believed to be of earliest Permian age. Their published report includes the intriguingly cryptic statement that this outcrop was located "in an unnamed place which we afterward used to call the Wolf Camp." In another report, they elaborated, with no less intrigue, that

> *Wolfcamp is the site of an old dwelling place, just to the south of the two buttes about 6 ½ miles east and some 2 miles north of the east end of Leonard Mountain. The place is not now inhabited, but it is marked by an old open well some hundred feet deep. "Lobo" wolves are said to frequent the place.*

The formation they described had not previously been cataloged in geologic literature, and so this fabled site in the Glass Mountains became the type locality and namesake of the Wolfcamp Formation.

About 150 miles north of the Glass Mountains, in the subsurface of the Permian Basin, the Wolfcamp Formation is similar to its type locality, and is composed of organic-rich shales and silty detrital limestones. The top of the Wolfcamp in the deeper Midland Basin occurs at 8000–10,000 feet below the surface, and the formation is 1000–1500 feet thick; in the deep Delaware Basin, the formation top is at 10,000–12,000 feet, and the thickness exceeds 6000 feet in places. Wolfcamp porosity in both basins generally ranges from effectively zero to about 10%. Its permeability is very low, although in many areas it is augmented by natural fracturing. Up on the platform, the Wolfcamp is quite different: it occurs at shallower depths, is only a few hundred feet thick, and is in many places composed largely of high-porosity, high-permeability limestone. The petroleum community long believed that the Wolfcamp was economically productive only on the platform, but recent development has proven that the formation is a money-maker down in both basins, although the thickness and quality of the productive intervals are variable.

Immediately overlying the Wolfcamp, and therefore younger in geologic age, is the *Dean Formation*. The Dean is relatively thin, ranging from 50 to 120 feet, and composed almost entirely of siltstone. Although it does produce oil in a few areas—we will briefly meet the Dean later in the story—it is not an important player on the Permian stage, and so we will move onward and upward.

The *Spraberry Formation* overlies the Dean, and its top occurs at a depth of 6500–8500 feet in the Midland Basin. It consists of 1100–1800 feet of sandstones, siltstones and shales and has less carbonate than the Wolfcamp below. Recall that the Spraberry time-equivalent package on the Delaware side of the platform is named the *Bone Spring Formation*. The Bone Spring top occurs 8,000–11,000 feet below the surface and in some places reaches more than 3000 feet in thickness. Spraberry sandstones have generally low porosity of 5–10%, and also low permeability, in the range of a millidarcy or less. However, as with the Wolfcamp, much of the Spraberry is naturally fractured.

The backstory of the Spraberry's name is not nearly as interesting as the Wolfcamp's. In 1944, when little drilling had been done in the basin and only shallow reservoirs had been found, the Seaboard Oil Company drilled a deep test well in Dawson County to obtain information about the potential for oil below the established San Andres reservoir. The farm on which Seaboard drilled the well was owned by one Abner Spraberry, and the well was named after him. During the drilling, at a depth of about 7000 feet, the bit penetrated a sandstone that produced a slight show of oil, and the zone became known informally as "the Spraberry sandstone." Seaboard did not attempt to produce the well, and for the next five years, no one paid much attention to the area.

Then, in early 1949, two wells were drilled and completed in the Spraberry sandstone, one by Seaboard in Dawson County and the other by the Tex-Harvey Oil Company about seventy miles south in Midland. The initial production was not spectacular, but drillers realized that the geologic similarity of the zone in the two wells, and its layer-cake continuity over the miles between them, pretty much proved that all the intervening area would likewise be productive, and a Spraberry play kicked into gear. As development spread, some highly productive areas were found. But due to the formation's generally low permeability, even when enhanced by natural and induced fractures, much of the trend proved to be only marginally profitable. Drillers had to minimize their drilling expenses to render the wells economic, and the formation was sarcastically regarded as "the world's largest unrecoverable oil reserve."

Notwithstanding its ho-hum economics, the Spraberry played a seminal role in the beginning of the Henry story, as you have seen. The formation continued to be a staple for Henry Petroleum, John Cox, Parker & Parsley and other operators for years. The Wolfcamp, on the other hand, was considered a tease. It occasionally yielded shows of oil while drilling and in drill-stem tests, but generally produced little oil when completed. Consequently, the Wolfcamp was largely ignored for decades. But in 2003, Henry found a key to unlock the formation's enormous cache of reserves. No one ignores it now.

Having established some familiarity with geo-speak, we will rejoin the Henry story already in progress. And by the way, now you're a geologist!

Chapter 4
From Austin to Appalachia

LIFE WENT ON after Bob. Jim and his company drilled a nine-well Spraberry program in late 1977 and planned a seven-well package for 1978. But Jim had begun to worry that the Spraberry might be picked over. "I was no longer content in the Permian. We had drilled several poor Spraberry wells close to Midland and couldn't find acreage at any good locations, so we were looking for some new place to drill." In the summer of that year, Jim's friend and local oilman, Tom Coffman, brought him a candidate.

The Austin Chalk is a group of formations in south-central Texas, named for the capital city where its most definitive outcrops occur. The strata are from the Upper Cretaceous period, much younger than the Permian. *Chalk* is a type of limestone, composed of microscopic particles of calcium carbonate called *coccoliths*, which are biologically secreted by phytoplankton called *coccolithophores*—what else? Coccolithophores are generated in untold billions in tropical seas. As they die, their soft parts decay, and the disarticulated coccoliths rain down on the ocean floor.

When conditions are right, thick deposits of the microfossils are lithified and form massive, blocky beds in the geologic record. The White Cliffs of Dover are an outstanding example of chalk. And for the record, this geological chalk is the original stuff used for cave drawings and blackboards—the modern material is a synthetic derivative.

Oil was discovered in the Austin Chalk back in the 1920s, but its producing rates and reserves were too low to attract development. Given its micro-clastic composition, chalk is understandably very *tite* (recall your Rocks for Jocks: low permeability). The Austin Chalk would not have produced at all were it not for a network of natural fractures connecting it with the Eagle Ford Shale source beds below it: the fractures provided both porosity for storing the oil and permeable passageways to connect it to the wellbore. Success at a given Chalk location was contingent on the well happening to penetrate a substantial network of natural fractures, so the play was very risky.

But in the mid-70s, spurred on by higher oil prices, operators began using two-dimensional seismic surveys (called *2D*) to locate flexures in the strata as an indicator of existing fractures. They also deployed hydraulic fracturing of the formation to create more cracks. By 1979, the play was hot. Operators developed two giant fields in the south-central part of the state: Giddings in the east, anchored in Brazos and Burleson counties, and Pearsall, centered in Dimmit and Frio counties about 200 miles to the west. Tom Coffman speculated that the two trends would eventually grow together, and he had identified twenty sections halfway between them in Wilson and Karnes counties, southeast of San Antonio. Tom pitched his idea, and Jim threw in.

Jim soon found himself in a new world. The leases there had names like Moczygemba, Kosciusko and Kopecki, very strange compared to good ol' Permian Basin familiars like University and Yates. And the terrain was different from arid West Texas: there was a *river* flowing across the prospect! The property was 400 miles from Midland, so Jim and his team would be operating remotely and relying on contractors and vendors with whom they had no track record. Jim was not worried about the remoteness of the venture: "I don't know if 'nervous' is the right word. More like *excited!* We were pioneering a new play for us which could turn out to be great!"

Jim drilled Henry's first two Chalk wells late in 1979, the Patton #1 in Karnes County and the Pruske #1 in Wilson. Both achieved excellent results. Based on this promising start, he pivoted most of the company's efforts and dollars to the south for the next two years.

To assist with Henry's growth and expanding operations, the company hired additional help. In August 1980, Red Daugherty tagged James Ray "Buddy" Martin and sent him to the Chalk project because, as it turned out, the company couldn't rely on the contractors down there. Buddy had thirty years of experience on both drilling and workover rigs, and Red knew the program was safe on his watch. Early in 1981, Jim hired Al Langford, founder and first president of Midland College, to aid in fundraising and investor relations. In September, the company hired a perky, part-time, vocational education student named Laurie Edmiston (now Richards) to woman the reception desk. Laurie was seventeen and beginning her senior year in high school. She later survived a royal rebuke by Harold Meredith and became Jim's secretary.

All these folks helped Henry take a big step forward. But in December 1980, Jim hired a man of singular significance.

Dennis Johnson is a "good Ag" petroleum engineer. After graduating in the mid-70s, he worked with Exxon for three years and then migrated to Union Texas in Houston. There, he climbed the ladder to the post of engineering manager of the Houston District. He then transferred to Midland to occupy the corresponding post in that district, and in 1979 rose further to district operations manager. The following year, Union Texas began discussing with Dennis the possibility of a transfer back to Houston. Dennis and his wife, Laquita, had a young child and preferred to stay in the smaller city. So he began shopping around.

Dennis also happens to be Jim's brother-in-law—Paula and Laquita are sisters. Jim and Dennis, who is not quite twenty years younger than Jim, had known each other for about a decade, mainly through family holiday gatherings and their shared love of tennis. And Laquita had worked for a while as a receptionist for Henry & Landenberger and then Henry Petroleum.

Oil prices were relatively high at the time, trending in the $35–40 per barrel range (about $100 in today's dollars). Companies were competing for good people, offering significant incentives to draw them in. A few independents were even allowing key employees to invest their own money in projects alongside the company, at the same or similar terms—a perk known as *participation*. Dennis had short-listed two companies, both of which included participation in their benefits packages, and he asked his brother-in-law's opinion. "Since Jim and I were both petroleum engineers," he said, "we often talked about the oil business. And I knew we shared the same Christian values and family priorities. So I asked him for his advice on the offers."

Henry was drilling the Chalk by then, and Jim had been thinking about creating a manager position to oversee development both locally and down south. He considered Dennis. But the family tie might be tricky: "I knew that if I hired Dennis, I could never fire him—if I did, I might have to look for another wife." Jim asked Dennis not to decide just yet, and set to work creating an incentive package that might lure Dennis away from the other two companies. At the time, Henry had no employee participation arrangement, but Jim knew he now needed one, not only to entice Dennis but to attract and retain quality employees going forward.

Meanwhile, Dennis contemplated the familial risks as well: "Although Jim and I had always enjoyed each other's friendship, families working together could get complicated." Blood relation notwithstanding, Jim felt he could not pass on the opportunity to hire "such a good, smart man." Dennis also saw the gain as greater than the risk: "We talked about keeping the company's financials and discussions at work, and keeping each family's personal business at home. This seemed to be workable for both of us." In the next few days, Jim made Dennis an offer that exceeded the other two in salary and benefits, complete with participation options. Both men saw clearly that it was ordained to be, and, as Dennis said, "We sealed the deal in short order."

Dennis joined Henry on December 1 as VP of drilling and production. In the light of later events, Jim's decision to offer, and Dennis's to accept, were two of the best decisions the men would ever make.

———————————

Dennis's onboarding brought another blessing to Jim and ultimately to the entire Permian Basin community: suddenly Jim had free time, and he viewed this as an opportunity not for relaxation, but for avocation. He had been attracted by politics for some time, and now he mulled the possibility of pursuing public office. But he also had a growing interest in volunteer nonprofit work: "I have a Christian background. I grew up in church. I wanted to take the Christian view and somehow give to those less fortunate."

As always, Jim listed the pros and cons of the two options, and then—also as always—he took the matter to his wise wife. "I told Paula, 'With Dennis here, I'm not going to have as much to do at the company, so I want to undertake something new. I can either go into philanthropy, or I can go into politics. Which do you advise?' And she said, 'Well, you're not going into politics!' And that was that. I agreed—I don't think I'd have made too good a politician."

In the spring of 1983, Jim submitted himself to United Way Midland and joined an Allocations Committee panel. He had chosen a post "fairly close to the bottom" because he wanted to learn from the ground up. An allocations panel consists of a handful of volunteers who vet the agencies supported by the UW, both to ensure that the agencies are doing what they pledged to do, and to determine appropriate funding amounts. Jim was a little beyond his ken at first: "The nonprofit world is different, it's a world all to itself." But he loved it and learned quickly.

He remembers one early lesson in particular. "The person in charge of the agency, the executive director, is critical to its success. You've gotta be sure you've got a good one because a nonprofit sinks or swims based on the quality of its director." That lesson would inform Jim and Paula's decision about staffing their own foundation thirty years later.

So commenced the Henrys' dedicated and meaningful service to philanthropy. They continue it to this day.

After the excellent results of the first two Chalk producers, the program had not proceeded well. The contract superintendent Jim initially hired proved to be untrustworthy, routinely boiler-plating reports and fabricating results. Not only that, but the man was not even showing up to supervise the completion work, and Jim suspected that the poor production results were due to completions being conducted on the wrong zones.

Jim sent Buddy Martin to the scene, to serve as Henry's eyes-on and superintend the *pulling units* himself. (A pulling unit, also called a *well service unit* or *workover rig*, is a truck-mounted rig used in completing and repairing existing wells.) But Buddy could not oversee all the operations, and Dennis also dispatched Pete Peterson to the project. From that point, the team was at least assured that the completions were being conducted as they had been prescribed.

But even with Henry personnel superintending the activity, the new wells were disappointing. Many were *wet* from the start (producing no oil or gas, only water) or watered out soon after. Henry's investors began to grumble. To fund his foray into the Chalk, Jim had established an investor pool different from his Spraberry projects, mostly small-time individuals new to the oil scene rather than partnerships and family offices that understood the risks of drilling. Some of the folks accused Henry of ruining the wells with poorly designed completions. Exasperated by this accusation, Dennis Johnson designed and conducted a test that proved the problem was not Henry's completion design but that the reservoir's existing natural fractures already reached downward into water-bearing strata. Dennis and Jim took this information back to the investors, and they all agreed to shut down the program.

Even this proof did not placate everybody. One investor from Odessa who did not quite get all his money back demanded that Henry return his investment. Jim was inclined to argue Henry's position. But Gary Wisener, Henry's retained counsel, advised him otherwise: "Just give him his money back. Even if you do prevail, the legal bill will be higher than the investment." So Jim wrote a check and vowed never again to go the small investor route.

Henry had drilled twenty-four Chalk wells when Jim and Dennis pulled the plug on the play. Of the lot, seven were dry holes, and many others quickly watered out or depleted. Buddy completed the last one, the Chandler #1 in Wilson County, in early April 1982—fittingly, it was a dud. All in, the project was about break-even. By summer 1982, it was time to head back to the Permian Basin.

By way of West Virginia.

———————

Bob Landenberger had continued to hunt and peck for prospects after the partnership dissolved, and Jim was happy to have him on a retainer both for the exposure to potential deals and to help his old friend. In early 1981, a Devonian shale gas play was heating up in central Appalachia. Bob brought the idea to Jim and Dennis, and the three decided it was worth testing.

The Ohio Shale is late Devonian in age, much older than the Permian. Its type locality is in the county of Devon, in southwest England. Like the Austin Chalk, the Ohio Shale requires naturally existing fractures to be productive. Where Bob was prospecting in western West Virginia and eastern Ohio, the top of the formation is at about 2500 feet below the surface, and about that same thickness. Because the shale was near the surface, prospectors used low-altitude, high-resolution satellite images of the earth (called *landsat*) to locate *lineaments*—large-scale "scars" resulting from tectonic faulting and flexing—as indicators of fractured zones. If the surface was fractured, there was a good chance the subsurface shale also was.

So the team bought landsat data and leased acreage along the lineaments that Bob identified as prospective. They assembled a leasehold position on both sides of the Ohio River in Washington County, Ohio, and Pleasants and Ritchie Counties in West Virginia. That's a long way from Midland, but the far afield didn't bother Jim and Dennis. Dennis had earlier been Union Texas's representative in the drilling of a Texaco-operated prospect about 100 miles offshore, east of Atlantic City. "So," he said, "a 5000-foot well in Ohio is no big deal."

But Appalachia did have its problems. "It was very hard to get information," Jim remembered. "There were very poor records kept by the state agencies." Dennis recalled that "the terrain was extremely rough. All the trucks used in the completions [the mobile pumping equipment and fluid transports] had to be short bobtail trucks because that's all that could make it on the switchback roads." And the mechanical equipment was yesteryear: "The pulling units were so primitive we had a difficult time completing the wells.

So we sent Buddy and Pete up there, and they found a welder and roustabout crew, and rebuilt the pulling units to our specs."

Then there were the locals. "Area operators often complained that they couldn't get their gas to the sales outlet because the mountain residents would 'hot tap' the sales line (siphon gas for their personal use). Because of all the trees and terrain, they could easily find a place to tap into the lines without being seen."

There were cultural oddities as well. "Many of the houses had no doors," Dennis said, "so their animals went in and out with the people." He remembered one encounter particularly: "We had drilled a well and were going to complete it, and there was a house about 100 yards away. The family had pulled up a stump about halfway between the well and their house, and often we'd see a family member sitting there, just watching. One day the wife was sitting on the stump. And her husband walked up beside her and *whammed* her across the shoulder with his forearm and knocked her off the stump, and then sat down himself. Our foreman was concerned about this, and went over and asked the man, 'Why did you hit your wife?' The guy said, 'Cuz she was settin' on my stump!'"

Local culture notwithstanding, it was poor reservoir quality that ultimately killed the project, as the Ohio Shale proved too tite to produce enough oil. Henry permitted six wells but drilled only two, both in West Virginia, from July to October 1981. Neither was economic, and the wells were soon released to the farm owners for personal use. Let them deal with their hot-tapping neighbors.

Henry had struck out in both of its step-out ventures to South Texas and West Virginia. Interestingly, both areas are producing prolifically today after being unlocked by a combination of horizontal drilling and slickwater fracking. Henry's vertical Chalk well on the Moczygemba lease had produced only 25 BOPD in December 1982. In late 2015, EnerVest drilled horizontally on the same lease and initially made 2946 BOPD—more than a hundred-fold increase. And on Henry's discarded acreage in West Virginia, the Marcellus and Utica Shales (both below the Ohio Shale) are yielding gas rates up to 10 MMCFGD. If Jim had only drilled a little deeper and taken a hard right turn, he and Paula might have struck it rich.

Well, might have struck it rich sooner.

By summer 1982, Henry had abandoned its imperialistic quest and was again focused on the Permian Basin. The company's asset base continued to grow through Spraberry drilling programs, and Jim and Dennis hired more folks to staff it. They picked up Kent Weber, an engineer and fellow Aggie whom Dennis had worked with at Exxon, and installed him as engineering manager, and they hired Dave Miller from Exxon to serve as geology manager. Harold Meredith, by now 68, was finding it harder to climb the drilling rig steps, and suggested that maybe it was time to retire. But Harold was far too family to let go, and Jim gave him an office position scrutinizing and ledgering invoices (a seemingly humdrum role at which Harold soon rose to legendary heights). To backfill Harold's field responsibilities, Dennis hired "AT" Fry, whom he had known during his days at Union Texas. And on the first of November 1982, the company picked up an enduring field hand. Dick Madison's son, Roy, had been pumping a handful of Henry wells during his high school years under his father's supervision. Roy had impressed Henry's field team with his dependability and can-do smarts. They offered him a contract job pumping a much larger beat, and Roy accepted (more tales of Roy also in a later chapter).

The company had more physical room now, having left the Petroleum Building in 1981 for a newly constructed edifice at 601 Marienfeld. Jim and Paula had owned the tract upon which that building was to be constructed, as well as the historic house which then occupied it. They relocated the house, and a group of investors erected the five-story building in its place. Although Henry no longer resides there, the building is still in use today. Locals refer to it as "the Belgian waffle" because it looks like, well, a Belgian waffle.

By now Dennis had taken on more and broader responsibilities and was stewarding all things excellently. He was able to think outside the Spraberry box, and began introducing new business strategies and technical procedures to the company. Jim decided to demonstrate his appreciation in a big way. "I had never before and never since allowed any employee to own an interest in the company. But Dennis was special and was doing such a good job." So in 1986, Jim arranged for Dennis to gain an increasing interest in Henry over time: "Eventually he owned about a quarter of the company, part of which we gave him and part of which we sold him at a very discounted price."

During this period, Henry generated two to four Spraberry drilling programs each year, each containing eight to twelve wells. Jim and Dennis sold the programs to their investors under the now-standard Ol' 7 and 7 structure. They always created a large program for yearend, for which the investors pre-paid in order to capture the tax deferral benefits. The company drilled eighteen wells in 1982 and nineteen in 1983, raising the company's total operated well count to 130. The company then drilled forty-six wells in 1984, a record that held until the Wolfberry blitz in the early 2000s. Henry's geographical footprint had expanded southward into Reagan County. Still more people were needed to manage the company's swelling asset, and the hiring continued. Early in 1984, Dennis hired Bob Dimit to serve as a staff engineer, and then geological manager Gary Weber (no relation to engineering manager Kent Weber) to replace Dave Miller, who had left the building.

Henry also picked up an excellent investor during that time. Green Bay Packaging is a pulp, paper and cardboard company privately owned by the Kress family in Wisconsin. (Not to be confused with the football team from the same city—the names are remarkably similar but, interestingly, the NFL Packers were named for a company engaged in meatpacking, an industry unrelated to paper packaging.) The Kress family office, then headed by Jim and Don, sons of founder George Kress, was investing in oil and gas for diversification. They were introduced to Henry by a Midland oilman who recognized a good fit between Henry's business model and the Kresses' desire for low-risk, predictable drilling programs. The Kress family was a true kindred spirit. "They were tremendous people to work with," Jim said, "very family-oriented, great partners." Dennis affirms the same but saw one problem with the relationship: "Jim and I really respected those men as individuals and how they ran their company. But most of our meetings were held in Green Bay, Wisconsin, and it seems that most of them ended up in the middle of the *winter!*" Henry's relationship with the Kress family would continue for more than twenty-five years and extend to other ventures.

Oil in early 1984 was trading in the $28 per barrel range after steadily descending from $40 in 1980. But the consensus speculation was that the price had reached a floor and would soon ascend again. "Every bank was then predicting that prices would continue to go up," Jim recalled. But not every*body* felt that way. One day, Jim's contact at New York Life called to discuss the oil price forecast. He told Jim that their consultant believed, contrary to the prevailing notion, that prices might actually tumble. "Who is your consultant?" Jim asked. "Henry Groppe," his contact said. "Do you want to see a copy of his report?"

Groppe, an engineering graduate of the University of Texas, had founded his consulting firm thirty years earlier and earned a reputation as a sage prognosticator. Jim was impressed with the global-scale breadth and postage-stamp detail of Groppe's research. He was also concerned with Groppe's forecast. Henry had taken on a manageable amount of debt and was servicing it responsibly at the time. But lower oil prices would make that difficult, if not impossible. "I thought, Groppe is probably wrong, but if he's right, then I'm going to go out of business—and I'm not willing to make this wager." Jim liquidated about half of the company's production, paid off the debt, and used the balance to fund Henry's current drilling programs.

In the light of what happened just eighteen months later, this was the right move.

Chapter 5
Henry Petroleum Version 2.0

THE SPRABERRY SITUATION had not magically improved upon Jim's return to the Permian Basin. The number of economically drillable locations was still dwindling, and the play was still yielding a low rate of return.

Setting aside the reservoir's weaknesses, there was a core problem in Henry's Ol' 7 and 7 deal structure, one that could stall the company at any time. For the structure to work, Henry had to spend capital: they had to spend money to make money. As earlier explained, the first 7 in the formula denoted a fee, paid to Henry by the investors, in the amount of 7% of the AFE to drill a well. So, for a well cost of $300,000 (using back-in-the-day figures), Henry was paid $21,000. Henry applied these capital fees to the company's overhead: rent, utilities, general expenses and—the biggie—payroll.

Specifically, the office payroll. Because the field hands worked on a contract arrangement and were not employees, their cost could be billed out to investors as an expense. But the wages of the office employees had to be paid by Henry, and funding for that expense came predominantly from the drilling AFE fees. Henry also had revenue streams from its producing wells and from overhead fees charged to those wells. But as the company kept only a 10–12% working interest, and as the Spraberry produced at low rates, this revenue did not amount to much income. So the office staff was supported almost entirely by the 7% capital fees the company collected only when it spent capital.

And the office staff was steadily growing. With the headcount now at about forty, Henry had to drill a fair number of wells each year to keep them fed. That number was twenty-four: Henry needed a half a million dollars each year—24 wells times $21,000 in fees per well—to pay its people.

Here's the Achilles heel in the deal: If something prevented Henry from drilling wells—say, an oil price crash that turned investors away from the Spraberry programs—then Henry could not meet office payroll. Everyone at 601 Marienfeld was at risk.

None of this is intended to throw the deal structure under the bus. It had elevated Jim and Bob from hand-to-mouth consultants to self-sufficient oilmen. The Ol' 7 and 7 was a boss, a winner in its day.

But maybe its day had passed.

———————————

Notwithstanding the flaw in the Ol' 7 and 7, and certainly without any prescience of the global upheaval that would soon occur, Henry drilled on. In 1985 the company drilled thirty-two wells, off the previous year's record but still above average. As always, most of these were Spraberry wells, and a few poked a little deeper into the Wolfcamp and Strawn.

Henry's operated well count was now at about 180. Included in that number was the handful that Jim and Bob had originally drilled in the Phoenix Grayburg Field back in the 70s. Other

Phoenix operators had also drilled in the interim, and at the time there were about twenty-five wells in the field. Frank West, the Hanover Planning man, had suggested early that Jim increase his investment in Phoenix. Frank believed the Grayburg sand would make an excellent *waterflood* candidate. In a waterflood project, water is pumped down into the reservoir via wells called *injectors*, and because water and oil don't mix, the water pushes the oil ahead of it toward the producing wells. Skipping over the technical details, waterflooding is used to sweep more oil from the reservoir than it would produce by only the strength of its own pressure. Waterflooding is also called *secondary recovery*, as it is most often conducted after the reservoir has already produced by its own pressure deflation, which is called *primary recovery*.

Heeding Frank's advice back then, Jim and Bob had set about buying interests from other field operators and lease owners. In order to waterflood the field, they would need to *unitize* it. A *unit* is a state-regulated entity in which the several mineral owners and operators pool their interests and their money to implement a waterflood (or some other *additional recovery* project). Forming a unit with all owners involved is necessary for both technical and economic reasons: a flood works most effectively over a broad area including many producing wells, and with multiple owners to share the cost. But establishing a unit can be difficult, as all parties must agree on a sharing arrangement for the capital, expenses, reserves and revenues. Nevertheless, units are routinely formed and operated successfully, and Jim and Bob were undaunted.

The pair had bought what leases and production they could at the time. Which wasn't much: most of the owners were not amenable to selling because the field was still producing at a relatively high rate. And anyway, the owners did not want to risk "the two *ifs*," as Jim called the conditions necessary for success: "*If* we can unitize the field, and *if* the Grayburg will effectively flood." In

Jim's mind, these risks were small compared to the potential gain. But other owners saw them differently.

During the intervening years, Jim had remembered Frank's advice and continued to eye the Phoenix field as he operated his wells there. Now, in 1985, things were different. The field was making only about 85 BOPD from seventeen active wells and barely covering its operating expenses. Jim and Dennis saw in a Phoenix waterflood not only a potential source of needed revenue, but an opportunity to diversify from the Ol' 7 and 7 Spraberry routine. They extended offers, and several owners were happy to cash out. As Jim says, "It didn't cost us much at all."

As a result of the Phoenix buying spree, Henry ended up with about 40% ownership in the field, and was one of only three remaining owner-operators. With only a few parties to be included in the negotiation, the situation was propitious for a successful unitization agreement, and the Henry team prepared to approach the other owners.

Then something very bad happened.

———————

OPEC, the Organization of Petroleum Exporting Countries, is a cartel (call it what it is) of nations that produce a disproportionate amount of the world's oil supply. Most of the member nations are in the Middle East and Africa. In 1985, there were thirteen OPEC members. Then, as now, the *de facto* leader of the cartel was Saudi Arabia, by virtue of its role as the *swing producer*. That is, Saudi Arabia has a great amount of spare oil production capacity, enough existing wells and infrastructure to produce far in excess of its current rates. With relative ease, the country can significantly raise or lower the world's oil supply. If the oil price falls below the Saudis' comfort level, they can close a few faucets, which tightens supply and increases prices. And if the price rises too much, they can open up a few.

OPEC's world market share in late 1985 was about 30%, down from 50% five years earlier. To combat the group's decreasing market share and bolster falling prices, the Saudis pressured other OPEC members to lower the collective production rate. Each member was assigned a national production quota, a *pro rata* share of the total. Of course, this arrangement would only work if the members honored their assigned quotas. Also of course, many of them cheated.

Except the Saudis. In an effort to support their price target as the total production rate continued to rise, the Saudis progressively lowered their own rate to a level well under what they had agreed upon. But the price was still falling, and the reduction in revenue began to cripple the Saudis' economy. Finally, in the winter of 1985, they wearied of watching their neighbors increase their own worth at the Saudis' expense. Saudi Arabia opened wide its spigots and began flooding its sales points with cheap oil, in order to retake market share from the cheaters (and from non-OPEC nations that had benefitted under the previous scenario). In a mad scramble to hold onto their own market shares, the rest of the OPEC members let rip as well. Prices crashed.

The sickening *thud* was felt in Midland: West Texas crude had been $30.38 in November 1985. It bottomed at $10.42 in March 1986. That's a 66% drop. Two thirds. Ouch.

The Achilles tendon in the Ol' 7 and 7 snapped. Fortunately, by heeding Groppe's caution and liquidating the company's debt eighteen months earlier, Jim had averted any immediate danger of bankruptcy. But Henry's Spraberry programs were not economic in this scenario, and neither Henry nor its investors would drill money-losing wells. And Henry would not be able to pay its overhead without drilling wells.

Something had to change. Quickly.

As was his wont, Jim sought the wisdom of counselors.

Early in 1986, he attended an elite American Management Association conference in New York. Among the speakers at the venue was one Walter Scott, a Harvard MBA, who had been very successful in top management positions with several companies in the northeast. He found an outlet for his mentoring passion in the American Management Association, where he was a valued speaker for some twenty years.

Jim absorbed Walter's presentation and was drawn to more mentoring. He recalled lamenting that "we really didn't have anybody to bunk outside his office and learn how to run a business." Jim did the next best thing: he retained Walter to evaluate Henry Petroleum, and help the company chart a course through the current crisis and into the future.

Walter came to Henry's office in Midland in early 1986. He vetted the company's business model, perused the financial records and spent time with all the employees. At the conclusion of his assessment, he made three seminal recommendations. One of these would be particularly painful, and another particularly pleasant.

First, the company needed to restructure. In the current organization chart, Jim as president oversaw land, finance and the contract geologists, and Dennis as vice president oversaw engineering, drilling and production. But Walter said that Henry needed a single executive at the very top, a visionary, to guide the company's direction and have ultimate authority over major decisions. That position needed to be free from the distraction of day-to-day affairs. The company also needed a single position to oversee all the company's operations, the entire day-to-day agenda.

It was clear to the three men who must be where. Jim was of course the man for the top spot. He and Paula knew best what they wanted their company to be, and Jim had always been successful in fundraising and promoting the Henry brand. Dennis was excellently fitted for oversight of the company's operations.

Since hiring Dennis to manage engineering and operations, Jim had stacked more responsibilities on Dennis's platter, and Dennis had handled all of them well.

Jim retooled the president position and filled it himself. This move had the collateral benefit of allowing him more time to devote to his growing passion for nonprofit work. He appointed Dennis as executive vice president, with all departments reporting directly to him. And as part of the restructuring, Jim and Dennis conducted the next of Walter's prescribed action items. The painful one.

There had to be a layoff.

The company had some forty folks on its roster. By Jim and Dennis's reckoning, they needed to drop that number to about fifteen. "And that," remembered Dennis, "was going to entail a huge amount of sad and difficult conversations." Laurie Richards, the former vocational education student who was now Jim's secretary, recalled the event: "I remember us sitting in Jim's office, both of us crying, and him saying he would never allow that to happen again. Just watching what that did to Jim was heartbreaking."

As Jim saw it, he had abandoned his people. "I use the analogy of a lifeboat: the company is a lifeboat. And the sharks are out there, swimming around this lifeboat. And we had about forty people in the boat, but it would only hold about fifteen. So we threw twenty-five employees to the sharks. These people were depending on Henry for a living, and we let them down." A few weeks after the layoff, Paula picked up drive-through at a local burger joint, and the man at the window was one of Henry's former professional employees. She and Jim were deeply grieved. "Here I was, fat and happy," said Jim, "and they're out there working for McDonald's. That's not right. And I said, 'We're not ever going to do this again.'"

For the record, they haven't.

Walter's final recommendation was that Henry improve its hiring practices going forward. Jim had already implemented an employee participation agreement for Dennis and a few top managers. Walter recommended that they extend the plan to all the professional staff.

Then came the pleasant step. In addition to offering broader participation, Walter said the company should add a bonus program, one not only generous in its amount but in its breadth: Henry must share its profit with the employees. *All* of them. From the C-Suite to the reception desk. "Whenever you have an event where you make good money," Walter said, "you must share it with the employees—you can afford to do so because you've just made a profit." But there was no such onus when the company did not profit: "If you don't make good money, you don't have the obligation to share the wealth, so you won't be going into the hole."

In listening to Walter, Jim recalled an earlier plane trip, sitting next to a Wichita Falls man who was managing a small oil company for its owner. As the two talked shop, the man told Jim that he had greatly increased the value of the company over a fairly short period of time. "He said, 'I took the owner's net worth from about $5 million to $15 million.' And I said, 'That sounds great! How much of that did you get?' And he said, 'Zero.' I thought, 'That didn't sound right, it didn't sound ethical. Here's a man who tripled the value of another man's company, and he just gets paid salary.'"

So, at Walter's recommendation, Jim and Dennis created what they called an *incentive compensation program* (*IC* for short). The annual program has changed a bit through the years, but Jim and Paula continue it to the present. The metric Jim uses for determining the shared amount is *the increase in fair market value of the company*. "We calculate the net worth of the company every year. If it grows, we distribute 25% of the increase to our employees. If it doesn't grow, then they don't get anything."

Many companies have some sort of a bonus program, but they are often based on an arbitrary metric, such as the increase in producing rate or the amount of new reserves added to the company's ledger. And the bonuses are only given to some of the employees, mostly those in management. By using company valuation for Henry's metric, Jim tethers the program to the ultimate goal. And Jim and Paula share their profit not only with managers but with *all* their employees.

The IC program has been a great bounty to Henry's families through the years, and those families have in turn paid the blessing forward throughout the Midland community. And when Henry's Wolfberry play peaked three decades later, Jim and Paula's IC program gave a whole new meaning to the term "largesse."

With the restructuring done and the layoff passed, Jim and Dennis settled into their new roles. Jim had now served for three years on the United Way Allocations Committee, and he wanted a change of scenery. He decided to volunteer at the agency level on a directors' board, and he had become interested in Casa de Amigos (CDA). Jim interviewed with the agency's nomination committee in May. The committee was impressed with Jim, and Jim was impressed with CDA, particularly with the expertise of the agency's director.

Lael Cordes-Pitts had obtained her master's degree in social work from the University of North Carolina at Chapel Hill. She moved to Midland soon after, and in 1985 accepted the position as CDA's executive director. Although she had been at it for only a year, Jim saw that Lael was guiding the organization well and, recalling his earlier lesson about the importance of the executive director post, he marked CDA as an agency that would swim. He was successful in his bid for directorship, and the next year became the board president. He enjoyed serving with Lael, and he and Paula would later tap her to assist them in administering their own philanthropy.

In the middle of 1986, with cratered prices still bouncing along between $10 and $15, Dennis resumed working the Phoenix unitization effort, assisted by the two unrelated Webers, Kent in engineering and Gary in geology. Henry now had about 40% ownership in the field, which was, as Dennis described it, "a philosophical change in direction to keep this much interest internally in a project, as compared to the 10% interest we typically had kept in the Spraberry drillwells prior to 1985." But he and Jim were determined to diversify in both partnership structures and play types in order "to get more legs under the stool," as Dennis said. Waterflooding of the Phoenix Grayburg would check both of those boxes.

By June, Dennis and Kent had devised a sharing arrangement that they thought equitable to all the Phoenix owners. They passed the baton to Henry's in-house landman, Patricia Yell, to identify, inform and poll all the operators and working- and royalty-interest owners of the proposed arrangement. (By the way, *landman* is a nickname for *land management* professionals, regardless of whether they be land males or land females.) The team mailed ratification forms in June, and the response was very positive.

But there was a bully on the playground.

One of the operators, headquartered in The Woodlands north of Houston, high-centered the discussions at the outset by demanding a disproportionate share of the production. Although that company did not own a majority interest—it had only 6%, compared to Henry's 40%—it also insisted on being unit operator. To achieve its objective, the company's representatives disparaged Henry to the other owners, accusing Henry of high expenses and improper accounting practices.

Jim and Dennis were understandably angered but, as always, resolved to respond with facts instead of force. The Henry team gathered data and dialogued with the owners and operators for many months. Over time, more of the parties sided with Henry, but the one operator refused to budge. In January 1987, Jim penned an exasperated note-to-self, suggesting several tacks Henry could take to settle the issue. He seemed not to have much hope that any of them would work. "Cc Dennis," he scrawled at the bottom, "then file: Phoenix WF" and gave the note to Laurie.

Henry prevailed in the end. Not by any concession from the holdout, but because Henry made compromises in the interest of the greater good: the team was convinced the waterflood project would benefit all the owners, and they were not willing to forgo that blessing if some measure of sacrifice could secure it. On July 16, 1987, a year and a month after the ratifications went out, Dennis sent a grateful missive to the participants: 94% of the working interest owners and 92% of the royalty owners had executed the unit agreement, well in excess of the Railroad Commission's requirement for approval (the *Railroad Commission of Texas*, or *RRC*, is the state's regulatory agency over oil and gas drilling and production). Henry was elected to operate the flood. The bully, stubborn to the end, had not yet signed (the company did eventually sign, although at that point its endorsement was not needed). Henry went to hearing in early September, and on November 1— the Henry oil company's eighteenth anniversary—received official approval for the Phoenix Grayburg Unit waterflood.

The Henry team commenced implementation immediately and began injection in January, with the unit producing a modest 63 BOPD at startup. Kent Weber had forecasted that initial flood *response*—increasing oil rate resulting from water injection—would occur within a few months. In May, unit production popped up a little to about 70 BOPD and stayed there for three months, but by August there was no doubt: the rate climbed to 90 and continued on a steady incline, reaching 450 BOPD two years later. Engineer Bob Dimit all but teared up as he remembered the flood response: "It was tremendous. It was beautiful. It was perfect. You don't see many of those out there in the real world."

Despite oil prices still in the $15 range, the Phoenix response was a home run. As Jim and Dennis and the team had anticipated, the flood was a boon to all the owners—even to the bully. God causes His rain to fall on the just and the unjust alike. The Phoenix project marked several Henry firsts: the company had maintained a high ownership, planned and completed a unitization effort, and designed, implemented and operated a waterflood project. Clearly, Phoenix qualified as a stool leg. It was the beginning of new growth and a harbinger of good things to come.

True to its namesake, the Phoenix had risen a second time for Henry. There would later be a meaningful third.

In mid-1986, oil prices shakily rose above $15 as the bewildered global oil system attempted to reestablish a supply-demand balance. There was still a glut of oil on the market, and the cost of leases and oilfield services had consequently dropped in response. Jim and Dennis saw a window of opportunity and looked for ways to reposition the company for advancement. Dennis was thinking way outside the typical engineering box: he wanted to build a program of low-cost, low-risk exploration. For clarity, in the petroleum industry the term *exploration* describes the drilling of wells in areas where little or no production has already been established; *development* describes drilling in areas that are already producing, such as Henry's Sprayberry routine. Exploration requires a special skillset that Henry did not have at the time. No worry, geological manager Gary Weber told Dennis, "I have a friend who's the best geologist for doing what you want to do."

Dave Feavel was a semi-successful explorationist who had worked for several small entities during the previous decade. He had known and worked with Gary for much of that time. By now, the Feavels had their first child, and Dave's penchant for working at precarious prospect shops without employee benefits had worn thin with his wife. "Michelle told me, 'You need to get a job.' And I said, 'I *have* a job.' And she said, 'No, I mean a *job* job!'" It was at just this time that Dennis asked Gary to recommend a prospect generator. Dave joined Henry Petroleum on October 1, 1986.

Based on his knowledge of the Permian Basin, Dave determined to prospect for shallow sandstones in the Strawn Formation in Haskell County, and for small structural traps in the Ellenburger Formation in Borden and Garza Counties—"little bitty bumps" he called them. The opportunities should be numerous if not large, and the program should serve Jim and Dennis's desire for diversification. Over the next two years, Dave was a prospect machine, and investors were receptive: "I generated and sold prospects for enough to pay for Henry's interest in the wells and to pay my salary. We never had a problem selling them." But he did have a problem finding oil, as most of the holes were dry. Nevertheless, by virtue of his salary structure and success in selling his deals, Dave was expense-free exploration. He is very proud of his achievement: "I cost Henry nothing."

Of course, this is tongue in cheek. Dave is an exceptional oil-finder, and Dennis promoted him to geological manager when Gary Weber left in 1988. Dave brags about his oversight of Henry's geology department at the time: "I was in charge of an enormous mass of people: myself. I was it. Period."

———

Later in 1986, as Jim and Dennis reviewed their employee roster in the wake of the layoff, they determined to make use of the sad opportunity to improve the company's organizational structure. Notwithstanding continuing low oil prices, they hired Jay Bowden to run the accounting department, and the next year tagged Kaye Morelock as land manager during the Phoenix unitization effort.

Then, in mid-1988, Henry hired someone very special. Kent Weber left Henry to assist in managing his family's ranching enterprise, and the company needed to fill his engineering manager post. Van Temple was a rising-star engineer at Union Texas in Midland, soon due for transfer back to Houston. Van and his wife decided they would rather raise their family in Midland, and he discreetly asked his office cohort for help scouting a local job. One of Van's confidants, Gary Pitts, was a faithful member of a close-knit adult Sunday school class at Midland First Baptist. Among the other members were Dennis and Laquita Johnson. As Kent was leaving, Gary reached out to Dennis: "Would you like to hire a really good engineer?" Van began working for Henry on July 1.

Henry suffered a loss in early 1989. Just after finishing a round of golf at Ranchland Hills, operations manager AT Fry suffered a massive heart attack and died. His passing left a void at the top of Henry's operational team. Dennis suggested that Van handle both engineering and operations, but Van told him, "I'm not an operations guy. You need a real ops manager." Van knew the right man: Mike LaMonica, a friend at Union Texas. The interview went well, and Dennis hired Mike as operations manager in March.

Along with Dave Feavel, these three men were destined to be critical contributors to Henry's great Wolfberry epic: Van Temple and Mike LaMonica would play key roles in the engineering part of the play, and geophysicist Gary Pitts, who shows up here as a Sunday school friend working for a different company, would later join Henry and be the first to realize how and where the play could be made.

Oil prices in mid-1989 were hanging around $20, having rebounded from an aftershock dip to $14 in early 1988. But with the cost of land and services still correspondingly low and with the new staff members settled in, the Henry team was now full-on questing for opportunities to diversify the corporate portfolio. In the summer, they identified Moonlight, a small field a few miles northwest of the city limits, as an acquisition candidate.

Moonlight had eight wells, all drilled in the 80s by its owner, the Anschutz Corporation. The wells were deep, completed in the Ellenburger Formation at 13,000 feet. The total current production was only 75 BOPD. Geologist Dave and engineer Van saw in the deep, low oil-rate wells the potential for *plugback* reserves. In a plugback operation, a plug is placed over the depleted zone and a shallower formation, higher in the borehole, is completed and produced. Plugback programs are often attractive because the cost to work over an existing well is substantially less than the investment to drill a new one.

Negotiations ensued, and the parties finally arrived at a transaction price of $500,000. This was by far the largest purchase that Henry had ever made, and the team did some serious soul searching before inking the deal. As Dennis said, "I remember that Jim, Van and I had a very deep discussion, and we had to really reach as a company to be able to close this acquisition."

Henry closed the deal, and the team got to work implementing the plugback opportunities they had identified. In the end, they were able to lessen the field's oil decline and increase gas production by about 1 MMCFGD. Moonlight was by no means a company maker, but it did help to diversify Henry's portfolio, and it was profitable. It also served as a training project for acquisitions, which added a tool to the company's pouch that would become very helpful within the next few years.

At the same time the Henry team identified Moonlight, another opportunity identified them.

Green Bay Packaging, the kindred-spirit family office, had been investing in Henry's Spraberry programs for five years now. At one of their partnership meetings, Don Kress mentioned that Green

Bay was frequently receiving farmout requests for the minerals under their timberlands in the Arkoma region. To supply the pulp for their packaging plant in Wisconsin, the family had purchased 40,000 forested acres in western Arkansas and eastern Oklahoma. Now, a gas play was beginning to take off in the area, and operators were soliciting leases from Green Bay.

The family had a great idea. The paper dryers in their Green Bay factories ran on natural gas, and they had inadvertently secured potential gas reserves under their Arkoma forestlands. By virtue of the US natural gas marketing system, the family could produce gas in Arkoma and swap it for gas in Green Bay. This would provide them a physical hedge in the event of high gas prices: by using their own gas, they would be protected from high operating expenses.

The Kress family knew more about paper than petroleum, so Don asked Jim if Henry could help them determine a course of action. The group ultimately established the Arkoma JV (*joint venture*). In the arrangement, Henry would manage Green Bay's minerals under their forestlands, in return for a small percentage of all lease money the partnership took in from other operators, and a percentage of the royalty interest the partners retained in the projects. Henry also got a special, one-time fee for conducting a mineral study of Green Bay's entire acreage footprint.

None of Henry's staff had prior experience in Arkoma. Dave accordingly scouted for a geologist experienced in that region and found George Olson, who was then working for another company in Midland. Dave also hired an additional geologist, Midland native David Grace, to assist with Henry's other projects.

The company picked up a few more souls during the same time. Jim hired Judy Hadaway (later Christensen) as his executive assistant, who proved to be invaluable in her service and friendship to Jim and Paula for the next twenty years. Dennis hired Scott Bryant to head the land department when Kaye left in early 1990. And Scott, a few months later, did Henry an invaluable service by hiring his friend, landman Bill Fair, who was also destined to play an essential part in Henry's Wolfberry play.

Henry and Green Bay participated in the Arkoma project primarily by farming out a portion of the requested acreage, and taking a working interest in the rest. Most of the deals were moderate in size and yielded moderate success. But there were a few exceptions. "At one point," Dave recalled, "we looked at a $5 million deal. George and I recommended not to join, but the JV managers overruled us and took 20% of it. Henry made a lot on the fee, but the drilling was a bust. We wound up in several large deals, and if just one had come in, it would have made the whole project profitable. But not a one of them hit."

Henry tried its own hand at operating in Arkoma, drilling three Arkansas wells in the summer of 1990 and one more in early 1992. All were dry except one, which produced a little gas. Henry drilled one well in Oklahoma in 1994, the Reents #1 in Grady County, but it too was dry. The Reents was Henry's final operated drillwell in the Arkoma project.

Henry's Arkoma drilling operations were not only disappointing, but at times a little suspenseful. "They had a big bombing range outside of Fort Smith," remembers Bob Dimit, "and you could only drill three months out of the year because the other nine months were when they were doing bomb drops. And there was still live ammo out there, so you had to be real careful." How does one be "real careful" in such a situation? "We hired people to sweep it for us." There's no action so careful as letting someone else take the risk.

In the end, the partnership did make money, but it was small reward for the effort. For the third time, Henry had ventured outside the Permian Basin to engage in a play beginning with the letter A, and for the third time had returned without much to show for it. But Henry had assisted their good partner Green Bay in evaluating their asset and monetizing it as best they could. And the training was worthwhile: a new area, remote at that, geologically complex and requiring engineering practices different from those in the Permian Basin. More skills in the skillset. And the Arkoma was yet another prop for the stool, a diversifier that ultimately carried on for more than a decade.

A final Arkoma note: as with Henry's failed Austin Chalk and Appalachian ventures, there is now a horizontal play—the Fayette-ville Shale—actively developing on Green Bay's forested acreage. The same acreage that Henry dry-holed.

By the early 90s, even with the efforts to become diversified, Henry Petroleum's asset base remained pretty homogenous. The Spraberry was still the company's main game, but no longer its only game. Of the new diversification projects, while only the Phoenix flood was bringing in substantial revenue, both Moonlight and Arkoma provided meaningful trickles and excellent training for the staff. In a move reflecting Henry's advance, in April 1991 the company vacated the Belgian waffle for a building that Jim bought on the then-outskirts of town at 3525 Andrews Highway. Henry is still there today.

Chapter 6
The Executive Office

FOR SOME UNKNOWN reason, in the world's corporate culture, the inhabitants of a company's C-Suite are referred to as "executives." Even though they don't execute anything. They fiat, decree, edict and enact, but they don't execute. They don't form an idea into concrete reality.

Execution does not happen up in the penthouse but down on *terra firma*. In construction, execution happens at the building site, in manufacturing at the plant, and in war on the battleground. In oil, execution happens in "the field." The true oil executives are the folks who drill the holes, pump the fracs, build the batteries and watch the wells. And from its earliest days, the Henry oil company has had some exceptional execs.

The first couple of men joined the Henry field team after they retired from previous careers and were in their late 50s and 60s. So these were "old school" guys, born in the first four decades of the twentieth century. (But bear in mind that old school is a moving window—millennials will be considered old school in twenty or thirty years.) The old school vintage of Henry's early crew was strikingly distinguished by its courage, resourcefulness, dependability and loyalty—traits which more recent generations woefully lack. On the other hand, today's contemporary priorities, such as social awareness, were not the old school's strong suit.

So, before they are introduced, a word of caution. Actually, a preemptive correction. Some of these men and some of their stories will appear crass from our twenty-first century perspective. But understand that these men were products of their time. They didn't have *Sesame Street*, James Dobson and the EPA to guide them. They were raised during the Great Depression and World War II, and they were instructed by these crises in a time when playing well with others was not nearly as essential as surviving. These men were taught to figure out what they needed to do, and to do it without whining. And they expected the people around them to do the same.

It is easy to slip into judgment of such people. It's easy to slip into judgment of a lot of things from the past, perched as we are on the higher vantage point of the present day. But to do so is to fall prey to what C. S. Lewis called "chronological snobbery" (in his book, *Surprised by Joy*, published in 1955. Lewis was also an old school guy, having been wounded on the front in France during World War I and survived Germany's bombing raids in London during World War II). Essentially, chronological snobbery is the uncritical assumption that whatever is contemporary is good simply by virtue of its being new, and whatever is old is inferior merely because it is old.

It turns out that we could not know what we know, nor be who we are, without the failures and successes and sacrifices of those who came before us. Bernard of Chartres, the twelfth-century French philosopher—that's *way* old school—makes the point profoundly: "We are like dwarfs seated on the shoulders of giants; we see more things than the ancients and things more distant, but this is due neither to the sharpness of our own sight nor the greatness of our own stature, but because we are raised and borne aloft on that giant mass."

In any case, don't overlook the fact that we today also are products of our time. As Lewis says, "Our own age is also 'a period,' and certainly has, like all periods, its own characteristic illusions." Fortunately, the illusions and errant priorities of today will be corrected by the better priorities of coming generations.

With your perspective now properly focused, read on.

———————

Harold Dee Meredith was born in 1914. That landed him smack in the center of what Tom Brokaw called "the Greatest Generation," and Harold bore all of its characteristic marks. When the Second World War came to the United States on December 7, 1941, Harold dutifully enlisted in the Army. With the rank of technical sergeant, he took part in the Normandy Invasion at Omaha Beach and was awarded a Bronze Star Medal for heroism (his brother Lee, younger by two years, fought in the Battle of the Bulge).

When the war ended, Harold returned to his pre-war job on a drilling rig for Amerada Petroleum. He brought all his great lessons with him. For twenty-nine years, Harold drilled wells in basins all over the country, living on location for weeks at a time under all manner of conditions and in every kind of weather. He retired from Amerada with full benefits in 1971, at the age of 58. Red Dougherty, Jim's quasi-operations man at that time, had worked with Harold at Amerada and knew his abilities. So in 1972, when Henry & Landenberger embarked on its initial operating enterprise and needed a field man to carry them forward, Red called Harold. Harold was a paragon of integrity. Jim describes him as "extremely honest." The foreman working for Jim at the time was "dishonest and incompetent, and he needed to be replaced. When we hired Harold, we went from darkness to daylight."

Harold was jealous for the welfare of Jim and Paula's oil company. "Whatever you did, you weren't going to cheat Mr. Henry if Harold had anything to do with it," Roy Madison recalled. Mike LaMonica described Harold as "incredibly loyal to Jim Henry. Incredibly loyal. Just a good man." Late in his time with Henry, when Harold was no longer able to climb rig steps and Jim gave him a job in the office, he remained vigilant. Bob Howard, an engineer and manager with Baker Atlas and its litany of precursors, had been doing wireline work for Jim since back in the Henry & Landenberger days. "Harold checked all the invoices that came in the door, and God help you if it was fifty cents more than the bid! He would call you and yell at you for five minutes over fifty cents. He never called me for undercharging—if it was in Henry's favor, he wouldn't say a word. But if you were over that bid, there better be a damn good reason!"

Harold carried into the oilfield the same selfless bravery and can-do attitude that had won him the Bronze Star at Normandy. On two separate occasions during his early employment, Henry's oil tanks were hit by lightning and caught fire (this is not uncommon). The tanks were fortunately full in both instances; otherwise, they likely would have exploded. But the hatches had been left open, and the escaping vapors ignited and were burning. In both cases, Harold scaled the tank's steel steps and closed the hatch, which smothered the fire. He was not being reckless—he understood the situation, and he was executing the solution—but he was certainly being courageous.

Harold's work ethic was typical of the old school—his day started long before the sun was up and continued until it was down. And he demanded the same effort from those who worked for him. Mike LaMonica witnessed the legacy of Harold's tight ship: "What I remember when I started at Henry [as operations manager over the field foremen] was Pete Peterson and Buddy Martin coming into the office at 5:30 in the morning. They'd be sitting there until

I got there at about 7:00. And so I said, 'Why are you guys here this early? There's no reason to be here.' But they'd been doing it for years when they were working for Harold Meredith."

If Harold believed he was not getting the effort and quality he demanded, he was not afraid to enforce improvement. Engineer Bob Dimit recalls a scene on a workover rig one day: "I went out to oversee my part of the job, and Harold was going back and forth with one of the rig hands, a great big ol' boy. Harold was standing on the ground, and the hand was on the rig floor above him. And they were getting into it verbally, and the hand said, 'Mr. Meredith, if you weren't so old, I'd come down there and whip your ass!' And Harold said, 'By God, don't let my age make a coward out of you! Get your ass down here and let's find out who's the bigger boy!' And the guy backed down from skinny 70-something Harold."

Harold's memory was as singular as his character. His ability to recall facts and details bordered on eidetic. Mike LaMonica remembered a man calling about a well that Henry had sold him. The new owner rigged up on the well, started running pipe into the hole and discovered a problem. "He said, 'We're hitting something in the wellbore that isn't in the records.' And I go to Harold, and it's been ten, twenty—who knows how many years since the well was completed by Harold. He looks up at the ceiling and says, 'Yeah, we stuck a packer in there near the Clearfork'—he told us exactly what it was and how deep it was!"

Bob Dimit's story is more amazing still. Shortly after he joined Henry in 1984, Bob was assigned to oversee an operation on a Henry lease near Big Lake, and he asked operations manager AT Fry for directions. AT told him that the company did not have written directions to any of its leases and acknowledged that the situation needed a remedy. "So we walked down to Harold's office, and AT asked him to write directions to all of Henry's wells. Over the next month, Harold handwrote directions to every Henry well, by memory, to the tenth of a mile, and they were all *right!* More than two hundred wells. And every one of his directions started out, 'From Stanton, go…'" Bob doesn't know why all the directions started in Stanton—Harold lived in Midland.

Even Harold's diet was fascinating. Every time Bob Dimit was on location, Harold would come by to check on him. He always brought his own lunch: "The same lunch every day. In a sack. He'd pull out an onion, peel it, and eat it. Like an apple. Every day. And a thermos of coffee. That was his lunch: onion and coffee, every day. I'm convinced that's why he lived so long."

Harold's opinion of engineers was pretty low. Through all his years at Amerada and Henry, Harold's job as drilling and workover foreman had been to establish a stable, clean, functioning wellbore. But there was often some engineer in the office wanting to run a DST or a new kind of pump that interfered with Harold's prime objective. As a new-hire engineer, Bob Dimit said that for about a year, Harold responded to his cheery "good morning!" by ignoring him: "I was just a dumbass green engineer who did nothing but cause him problems."

But Harold was a fair man, not at all biased—he was equally averse to geologists. Dave Feavel recalls a day shortly after geological manager Gary Weber hired him: "I was sitting in my office next to Gary's, and Harold was down the hall in his invoice room. And I hollered next door to Gary, 'Hey, I'm going to need some business cards—what should my title be?' And Gary said, 'Oh I don't know, what about senior geologist?' I said, 'OK, that sounds good.' And Harold chirps from the room down the hall, 'I wouldn't be too damn proud of that!' He was kind of smiling when he said it."

As impeccable as was Harold's integrity, as inspiring his courage, as amazing his memory and as quirky his lunch, one skill above all else engraved Harold in the minds of those who knew him: the man was a butt-chewing wonder. At the mention of Harold's name, interviewees gravitated quickly to that theme, often within a few seconds. Whenever Harold believed that intentional or incompetent wrong had been done on a job, he would light into whichever poor soul he deemed the doer. And his ignition was instantaneous: no pre-heat, no fuse, only pure flashpoint—it was either off or it was all on.

Consistent with his old school respect for authority, Harold did not behave in such a manner toward his superiors. So Jim Henry was never a recipient of a Harold butt-chewing. But he did witness it: "Harold didn't really have a temper, but he would chew you out if you did something wrong, and you wouldn't do that something again. He would routinely chew out people in the field, especially if they charged too much for a job." Jim speaks graciously of his old friend, but his use of the adverb "routinely" is revealing.

Jim remembered one butt-chewing in particular: "Harold was the completion foreman on a well in Andrews County that we had perforated and fracked, and the well was responding poorly. The investors had hired a consulting engineer to help with the evaluation, and he asked Harold, 'Are you sure you put the perfs in the right place?'" The consultant had inadvertently questioned Harold's competence. "Harold lit into him, and by the time he got done, there was no doubt in anyone's mind that those perforations were exactly where Harold said they were!"

Mike LaMonica, as Harold's boss, was likewise safe, but his assessment was more direct: "The vendors were terrified of him, because he could rip like nobody could rip." Bob Howard's claim, quoted above, that Harold yelled at vendors over fifty cents may seem like hyperbole, but Mike was eyewitness to an actual instance: "My office was across from Harold's. And one day, I'm hearing him scream at these vendors. And I go in there, and Harold's got this invoice in his hand. And I said, 'Harold, *what is wrong?!?*' And he says, 'These men charged us fifty cents more than they said they would!'"

Bob Howard was one of Henry's vendors: "When Harold got ahold of somebody, it was monumental. I worked for a wireline company for thirty years, and twenty of that was in sales. I know what good ass-chewin' is, and I tell you, Harold Meredith was world-class! I've had ass-chewin's you wouldn't believe, and Harold was top three at least. And the thing was, he *liked* me, he liked me *a lot*. One day we had some trouble on a job, and Harold started ranting and then said, 'Bob, if *you guys* can't do good on this job, *who can?!?*'"

Harold's rarefied mastication skill was never as great as when he believed a service company had been negligent with Henry's affairs. Roy Madison remembered an episode not long after he started pumping for Henry. One of the tanks on his beat was rapidly filling with oil, and the hauler had been unresponsive to Roy's repeated calls. So he called Harold: "I said, 'I've got two full tanks on the Stimson 84, and I'm about to have to shut it in. I can't get Permian to come pick it up. Can you help me?' And Harold said, 'You're damn right I can!' *Click!* In about ten minutes, the Permian guy called me and said, 'Roy, I don't know who that was that I just talked to, but don't you ever call him before you call me. He took enough out of my rear that I won't be able to sit down for a week!'"

Laurie Richards, the student at Henry's reception desk, was memorably introduced to Harold when he called in his daily report from a payphone: "Some man called collect, and I didn't know if I should be accepting a collect call from anyone. I remember saying, 'Let me check, please' and putting the operator on hold. I asked around and was told yes, accept the call, Harold works for us. When I got back on, I accepted the call, and as the operator was hanging up, I got a good butt-chewing! 'You better blankety-blank accept my call! Blah-blah-blah!' We laughed about it much later, but I was in tears at the time. I learned pretty quick to accept calls from Harold Meredith!"

Explosive as he was, the Henry folks—some of whom he had chewed out—also remember Harold's core of kindness. Johnny Brown, Henry's long-time lease operator, worked for Harold and described him as "a good ol' man. I screwed up a lot. And I'd call Harold, and he'd tell me, 'Well, did you learn from it?' And I'd say, 'Yessir.' And he'd say, 'Keep in mind that a man who don't ever screw up ain't doing very much work.'" And Laurie recovered fully (if not quickly) from her chew-out, and she and her children later became close friends with Harold: "He was such a nice man. He was like a grandfather to me, and my kids still giggle about their Harold stories."

Harold retired from Henry in June 2002 at age 88. He had pledged Jim "two or three years," Jim had requested twenty, and Harold had delivered thirty. He moved to his hometown, Stroud, Oklahoma, to live with his brother Lee and his family. Harold passed away in 2006—fittingly on Pearl Harbor Day—at age 92.

Like Harold, JC "Pete" Peterson was a member of the Greatest Generation, born at its tail end in August 1927. Pete also volunteered to serve in the Army during World War II, but he almost didn't get the chance. Pete relayed his story to Roy Madison: "When Pete tried to join the military, they told him you had to have a name, and his real name was just the letters, JC. And the military said, 'That's not gonna work.' And so Pete said, 'Well, call me 'Pete.'" And Pete Peterson was born. So to speak.

Jim hired Pete in March 1976, as a foreman to work under Harold in the company's Spraberry operations. Pete had exceptional pulling unit skills. "He was excellent," Jim recalls, and Johnny Brown remembers him for his particular expertise as "a money saver." But Pete, another product of his time, "was not a good people person," as one of the contractors put it. A few colleagues were more candid and described him as "rude" and "downright mean." Roy Madison admits that Pete was ever suspicious of his contractors. "He watched the pulling unit to the minute, he was crazy about that," Roy said, "and he wouldn't dare leave a job, thinking that the second he left they'd stop working. So if he had a doctor's appointment or something, he would just shut them down early. He didn't trust them at all."

But Pete's trust could be earned. Victor Jordan has worked on Henry wells as a pulling unit contractor for more than forty years. He acknowledged that Pete was "one of the hardest guys I ever had to work with. But I did just what he told me to do, just the way he wanted it done." Victor recalled one Pete episode, when he and his crew were cleaning out a fracked well near Greenwood. Because the well continued to kick, the men kept working into the evening, even though it was very cold. Victor asked his wife Julia, an excellent cook—she has often graced Henry's office with her breakfast tamales through the years—to deliver a chili-bowl dinner to the location "and bring some coffee for Pete. And he really appreciated that, and that's when he knew that I would take care of him and of Henry's business." Pete became Victor's biggest supporter: "He told everyone at Henry to call me if they needed help. 'If you got a well problem you can't figure out, call Victor, he'll take care of it.'"

Roy Madison, who worked under Pete, also saw him in a kinder light: "He wasn't mean, but he was very strict. And it was funny: when he got out of his truck and approached a pulling unit floor, there was no way he was gonna smile. And he would give them his orders, and then he'd walk back to the pickup. And it was like Dr. Jekyll and Mr. Hyde—he'd start right back to cutting up with me and he'd be laughing."

However surly Pete may have been, Jim's other foreman was smiley. Buddy Martin was born in 1932 and narrowly missed the Greatest Generation, but he was still an old school guy. Buddy served in the United States military during the Korean War, from 1951 to 1953. Jim hired Buddy in August 1980 to be his eyes on the Austin Chalk program.

Never did a man have a more appropriate nickname. Victor

called Buddy a "sugar bear," and Bob Dimit described him as "like a big, loveable teddy bear, a jolly fellow. He always laughed—no matter what he'd say, he always laughed after it." Bob also remembered Buddy's endearing stutter, as did Dennis Johnson: "Buddy talked with a great stutter. He was a big man at 6 feet 2 inches and 280 pounds, and when he got excited, he stuttered so much we couldn't understand him. Buddy did an excellent job for us. He was a very smart man with a heart of gold."

Buddy was always joking about something. "Buddy and Pete were both working down at the [Austin] Chalk, and it was really hot," Johnny Brown remembered. "And Buddy told me a story about it. He said to Pete, 'I need to hire out a road maintainer.' And Pete asked him, 'Why?' Buddy said, 'I need to clear out a circle around this well location here.' And Pete asked him, 'Why do you need a circle cleared?' Buddy said, 'Well, I get paid mileage on my truck. But sitting here parked and running the air conditioner without going anywhere is costing me money. If I get this location cleared, I can drive around in circles.'"

Pete and Buddy presented something of a good cop/bad cop team. Bob Dimit summarized: "Everybody wanted to work for Buddy, and nobody wanted to work for Pete." Johnny Brown remembered that "Buddy would get the rig crew started, lay back, and go to sleep. He wasn't worried about too much." From a vendor's perspective, Bob Howard recalled that "Buddy was much more efficient in getting work done than Pete, because Buddy could delegate and let people do their job. Pete was a micromanager, and he had his thumb on everything and just didn't have any people skills. Buddy told you what he wanted done and stayed out of your way. Pete told you what he wanted done and then he stood around and yelled at you if you didn't do it fast enough."

Roy Madison, who worked for Pete, has a mitigating viewpoint. "I almost hated to see Pete rigging up on one of my locations, because he always wanted to visit. He always wanted to talk. It was at least an hour every time I ran into him in the field. Every time. And Buddy Martin was just the opposite. If you drove up on Buddy, he wanted to get rid of you. Not to be mean. He just didn't like to visit."

Buddy left Henry in 1995 to tend his son, Virgil, who'd been diagnosed with a brain tumor. He was later able to consult for the company until 2000. Buddy passed away in March 2006.

Pete also retired in 2000. And however his pluses and minuses may have settled in the oilfield scales, in Pete's family he was, as his 2008 obituary described him, "a loving father, grandfather and great-grandfather." This must be true: Pete's granddaughter named her first baby girl after him. And she used his real name: JC.

When Harold's field days were done and he swapped his pulling units for a desk, he left a large hole in Henry's executive suite. Harold would be impossible to replicate, but Dennis Johnson believed that drilling superintendent AT Fry, whom he had known at Union Texas, would be a pretty good stand-in. AT had recently retired, but he told Dennis he was willing to work a few more years as operations manager.

Bob Howard had worked with AT for years as a service provider, and the two became close friends. "AT was all business at work," Bob said. "He was very efficient at what he did, and he was really good for Henry Petroleum." Outside of work, his friend was maybe not quite toe-the-line: "Fry was a Southern Baptist, occasionally." And like Harold and Pete, Bob admits that his friend also "was a little rough" on people who worked for him. Well, maybe more than a little: "He could sure chew ass. Now, he wasn't in Harold Meredith's class, but he was close."

Engineer Bob Dimit saw that side of AT one day at a Spraberry frac job: "One of the hands came up, a young guy, and said, 'Mr. Fry, I've heard stories about you, that you were a tough SOB to work for. But I wanted to let you know that I really enjoyed working for you today. It was a pleasure, and all those stories weren't true.'" AT took out his notebook and asked the young man's name. He wrote it down. "Then AT got in his face. 'Well, lemme tell you something. I am a tough SOB. I've worked for thirty-eight years in this industry to get that reputation and no snot-nosed kid is gonna ruin it for me! You will not ever be on a location of mine again!' And AT went to the crew foreman and told him to send the young man home."

AT died suddenly after a round of golf in the spring of 1989, and his passing was symbolic of a transition at the company, and in the culture at large. Baby Boomers—folks born between 1946 and 1964, twenty or thirty years after Pete and Buddy—are a bridge between the old school and contemporary times. They lived in the former world and have helped to tame it into the present one. At the time, Boomers had been entering the job market for a while. They showed up in Henry's executive office in the persons of Johnny Brown and Roy Madison.

Johnny was born in 1952. He enlisted in the Air Force during the Vietnam conflict, and served three years as an airplane mechanic flying hush-hush missions across the Pacific. When he left the service in November 1976, he and his wife, Donna, moved to Lamesa, where they both had family. Johnny had taken leave a few months earlier and found a job as a pumper, working for a man who was contract pumping some of Henry's wells. The man assigned the Henry wells to Johnny. One of those wells, by the way, was on the lease owned by Roy Tidwell, the farmer who had planted "Henry rows" in appreciation for the farm-saving income the well generated for him.

Mere adjectives like *dependable, conscientious* and *stalwart* do not begin to credit Johnny's commitment. During one span in his career, he worked a staggering twelve and a half years without taking a day off—4600 consecutive days. "We were contract pumpers, and if you wanted to take time off, you had to hire somebody to cover for you. I took off five days between Christmas and New Year's in 1982, and when I came back, the guy I had hired had taken off too. And that had happened two or three times to me in the past. So I decided, to heck with this! So from January 1983 till July of 1996, I didn't take off a single day, not a sick day, nothing."

During that span, Johnny maintained time with his wife and two children as a top priority. "On Saturdays, I'd go to work at two o'clock in the morning and go and run the lease, and I'd get home about ten. The kids had gotten the boat all loaded up and ready to go. So we'd hook onto it, drive over to Lake Spence or J.B. Thomas, and we'd play Saturday afternoon and night and Sunday morning. We'd leave about noon and come home, and they'd unload the boat while I went to run the lease. And then five o'clock Monday morning, it was back to the same thing. So I didn't miss a day."

By his own choice, Johnny had stuck with the same job in the same area for four and a half decades, without ever seeking to climb the company ladder (he declined promotions more than once). The reason for his choice is anchored in the day he was introduced to the job. When Johnny took Air Force leave to go to Lamesa and look for work, he visited first with his brother-in-law, who was a mechanic at a local car dealer. Johnny thought he might parlay his mechanic skills with airplanes into automobiles. But knowing the local industry, his brother suggested Johnny consider being an oilfield pumper: "I work on some of their trucks, so I've gotten to know some of them, and they make pretty good money." It sounded interesting enough to Johnny, so the brother introduced him to a friend, a contract pumper who happened to be Pete Peterson's son-in-law. "I rode through the lease with him that next day. And I just fell in love with it." What was it about the job? "I don't know. But I still love it. There's just something about it."

At Henry, Johnny was a valuable mentor both to young guys and to his bosses. Billy Bledsoe, Henry's current operations manager, referred to him as "the University of Johnny Brown": "He's a really good teacher. He's old school, and our young, emerging leaders in the field respect him and learn a lot from him." Billy attended Brown University himself, especially when he was promoted to manager and needed to learn more about pumpers' work: "Johnny taught me quite a bit about what that role does, what it should be doing, how best to accomplish our goals and where I was wrong. I really respect his knowledge and the solutions he proposes."

Johnny operated Henry's leases for forty-five years. He retired in April 2021. Johnny and Donna have got a home near—what else?—a lake in Central Texas. And for the record, only one employee of the Henry oil company has logged a longer tenure than Johnny Brown, and that is Jim Henry—and Jim has Johnny by only six years.

Roy Madison pumped a small beat of Henry wells for his father when Roy was in high school, and he earned a direct contract job with Henry in November 1982, working under Pete Peterson.

Roy was still with Henry as of summer of 2021, after forty years. By then, Billy Bledsoe affirms, "He has worked literally every job we have in the operations group," learning and performing all of them well: pumper, mechanic, facilities, drilling, logging, fishing, production and well stimulation. "He's also my most experienced guy with electrical construction and troubleshooting, my go-to man to get power lines run, meters set and contractors assigned." For much of his career, Roy had only one flaw as a worker: "If asked whether he can do something, Roy would always say yes. That was his greatest strength and his most glaring weakness. He would move heaven and earth to do what he was asked to do, and he'd work himself to exhaustion doing it." These days though, Roy is "much more realistic about what can and should be done, and he's quick to tell you when a request cannot be accomplished safely."

Back in the day, Billy said, "Roy ran everywhere he went." That epithet is spoken of Roy in the same way that "butt-chewing" is spoken of Harold. Roy owns it: "People say that I ran everywhere I went, and drove fast—well, I had to! If I wasn't running, I was falling behind! You almost have to run everywhere to get things done." Doug Smith worked for Henry as a drilling foreman at one of the fields Roy was pumping: "Roy ran everywhere he went. When he pulled up and got out of that pickup, he took off running. The first time I ever saw the guy I thought, 'What in the world is wrong with him?'" Doug soon got over his bewilderment, and the two became a strong team on Henry projects in the 90s and 00s. Doug echoes Billy's endorsement: "I just can't say enough good about him. There was nothing that I needed that that man wasn't willing to do."

Not all of Roy's running was for work. His daughter, Caroline, was once assigned an insect collection project at school, and Roy wanted to be of assistance. He was pumping a lease south of the landfill on Highway 158 during that time. "One day, I saw a big butterfly, and I started running through the pasture trying to catch that butterfly. And I would jump and try to grab it, and I probably chased it for fifteen or twenty minutes." Roy's expedition did not go unnoticed by the rancher, who caught up to him the next day at the tank battery. "He said, 'Are you alright, boy?' And I said 'Yessir.' And he said, 'I kind of wondered about you yesterday.' And I said, 'How's that?' And he goes, 'You were running out through the pasture, jumping around and clapping—what in the heck were you up to?'"

Like Johnny, Roy was determined not to allow his work schedule to rob him and his family of time together. He often took his children with him when he had an easy beat or a docile chore. And his wife, Faye, routinely accompanied him when she could spare the time. Once, when he planned to do some plumbing work at a tank battery, Roy asked Faye to join him. He didn't actually need help, but the two looked for such opportunities to spend time together. Doug Smith had recently joined Henry, and he stopped by to check on the progress as they were finishing the job. Roy made the introduction: "Doug, this is my wife, Faye." She was wearing shorts, a tank top and work gloves, and she had pipe grease all over her arms. "When she drove off, Doug said, 'What the hell are you doing?!? If you needed help, I would help you! You don't need to make her come out here.' And I said, 'Doug, you just saw her—she's a lot prettier than you, and she sure don't gripe as much. And besides, I didn't need help—this is *our* time.' When you work seven days a week, if you want to spend time with your family you bring them to work."

Roy later moved into the office and is currently Henry's operations superintendent under Billy. He doesn't run through the halls. But make no mistake—Roy is still an executive.

———————

There is one more member of Henry's executive team who deserves at least an honorable mention.

Jim Henry got his oilfield start as a roustabout, working one summer at a Humble field near Bronte, Texas. "When I first got on the crew, we piled into the truck and went out to a location, and the guys all grabbed shovels and started digging. And I was just standing there looking, because no one told me what we were doing. Well, when we went to the next location, I jumped out of the truck and grabbed a shovel and started digging. I just did it. Fortunately they did need a hole dug!" It's a fond memory: "I enjoyed being a roustabout. We had a lot of camaraderie in the crew, and the work was a lot of fun."

During the summer following his junior year at OU, Jim worked as a hand on a drilling rig. Then back at school in September, he signed up for his interview with Humble. The interviewer was impressed by his grades and extracurriculars—Jim had a 3.2 GPA and was president of Pi Epsilon Tau (PET), the petroleum engineering honor society—but he looked askance at Jim's drilling rig work. "The man said, 'That's pretty difficult work for a guy who's not any bigger than you are.' And I said, 'It's not the size of the dog in the fight, it's the size of the fight in the dog!' I think that impressed him." Humble gave Jim the job.

Of course, Jim has nothing like the field skills of the executive team described above, and he would never claim to. But he has seen some of the view from down below, and he has gotten his hands dirty.

Chapter 7
MIPs, Flips and Floods

HENRY HAD BEEN around for about twenty years when 1990 showed up on the calendar. The company had grown a bit over that period. One of the standard oil industry metrics for assessing the size of a company is well count. Since Henry & Landenberger drilled its first fifteen wells for the Hanover 6-6-3 project, the number had grown to about 250. On a relative scale, that number lands Henry in the "small independent" category of the Permian Basin hierarchy.

A more translatable metric for comparison with other enterprises is fair market value. Henry's climb from $0 had not been particularly steady. This is understandable, as volatile oil price is a prime control on a private company's valuation. The company had also been halved in 1977 when Bob Landenberger retired. Nevertheless, Henry had grown to about $1.8 million by the early 80s (in 1980 dollars) and, despite being briefly hammered by the crash of 1986, had sort of flattened out at that level for most of the decade.

But during the two years before 1990, the value increased

sharply. Oil had improved to the $20 range. The Phoenix field was a significant driver, as its production rate was climbing steeply in response to the flood. These factors, along with growing revenue from the increasing well count—from both the drilling and overhead fees paid by the investors, and Henry's owned portion of the oil and gas sales—had built up the value to the $6 million mark. Still, a $6 million fair market value was pretty small. Notwithstanding Phoenix and recent diversification forays into Moonlight and Arkoma, the Ol' 7 and 7 Spraberry was still the largest leg under the Henry stool, and it could only grow the business at a very slow rate.

Jim and Dennis needed a new growth vehicle, something bigger and faster.

In order to continue to be profitable and grow, major oil companies—the Exxons, Chevrons and Shells—need major projects. They pursue large assets with large potential, and they allocate their manpower accordingly. Meanwhile, their older, fully developed projects decline and eventually dwindle. These vintage properties may still have potential, but that potential is slight relative to the company's growth needs. And the work necessary to realize the potential is generally manpower intensive—opening small pay zones in producing wells, repairing damaged wells, and replacing and updating worn-out equipment and facilities. Consequently, many of these properties are neglected. From time to time, a major will cobble together some dwindling properties into a "sales package" and divest them. But at any given moment, the company may have a few of them limping about.

Dennis recognized substantial opportunity in this scenario, and he devised a business model for partnering with majors to squeeze more oil out of these older properties in such a way that both Henry and the major would profit. He called his model, Major Independent Partnering, or MIP for short (pronounced as a one-syllable word, *mip*). As Dennis explained: "The MIP concept involves Henry [the independent] first identifying potential in a field owned and operated by a major oil company. Then Henry proposes a capital work program to the major, with a deal structure that would be equitable for Henry to get a return on investment and for the major to improve its profitability." That improvement is most often in the form of increased production by drilling and *recompletion* programs (opening new zones in existing wells), but Henry also focused on reducing operating costs, improving the efficiency of facilities and infrastructure, and resolving potential liabilities, such as damaged and *shut-in* (idle) wells. Dennis's concept was modeled on similar arrangements becoming popular in the industry, but his was customized for Henry's skillset and goals.

Dennis began looking for large, old, neglected oil fields owned and operated by majors. But he didn't use a map—he used his Rolodex. Near the front, under A, was ARCO. Dennis was acquainted with several ARCO managers from various professional and personal circles. In particular, he knew Tony Best, ARCO's local head, from racquetball and industry meetings. Tony was open to Dennis's idea, and he suggested that ARCO's Shafter Lake property would serve as a suitable first project.

The Shafter Lake Field is a large, *multi-pay* (several producing formations) geological structure northwest of the city of Andrews, situated atop the Central Basin Platform. As with many other CBP fields, Shafter Lake was discovered in the 1930s, and initially produced from the San Andres reservoir, then subsequently found productive from the Ellenburger, at 12,000 feet, all the way up to the Yates, at 3000 feet. ARCO had acquired a moderate position in the field in the early 1980s, some 3800 acres, and they currently operated about seventy wells.

As Shafter Lake was old, large, multi-pay and operated by a major, there was little doubt of its neglected potential. Dave Feavel, by then Henry's geological manager, was involved in the negotiations: "ARCO felt like they had done everything that could be done with Shafter Lake. Back in the day, every new ARCO engineer that came into the Midland office was 'given the Shaft.' That's what they called it. ARCO management assigned the greenies to Shafter Lake."

Dennis proposed the establishment of a decline forecast for existing production, agreed upon by both companies, to serve as the baseline that Henry must exceed in order to share in the revenue. In other words, Henry's goal was to increase production and thereby deflect the currently declining trend upward—or as Dennis succinctly said, "We wanted to bend the curve." In this structure, ARCO would retain all the existing baseline production, and both Henry and ARCO would share in the buildup that Henry achieved through its capital programs, which Henry would fund. All the risk, then, was on Henry, and ARCO would benefit from the increased production without having to pay anything for it.

The Henry team intended to increase production mostly through recompletions and optimizing the operations, plus a few new drillwells. But there was additional potential. "In these discussions," Dennis recalled, "the possibility of a Clearfork Formation waterflood came up. The Clearfork needed more technical evaluation, and the concept evolved into Henry committing to drill test wells and gather geological data to assess the potential. And then after an evaluation period, Henry must either commit to a large-scale Clearfork waterflood or return the field to ARCO." Henry agreed, and the deal was signed in late 1992. Now Henry needed to find a way to pay for it.

Dennis called his Sunday school friend, Gary Pitts. Gary had since left Union Texas to join Neste, the national oil company of Finland, which had an office in Midland (true story). Gary recalled that he "was looking for stuff to get Neste into the Permian, because they mainly had offshore properties handled out of Houston. I saw the potential in the Shafter Lake MIP deal. So I asked Dennis,

'How much does Henry want to keep?' And he said, 'A third.' And I said, 'OK, we'll take the other two thirds.'" Notice here the increased ownership that Henry kept in this project, 33%, relative to the 10–15% retained in earlier Spraberry programs. The 1986 layoff had taught Jim and Dennis the necessity of higher cash flows, which required higher ownership.

Henry's operations team drilled five wells at Shafter Lake in early 1993, two in the San Andres, two in the Clearfork, and one in the Wolfcamp. They also completed several *workovers* (a general term for recompletions and repairs). Operations manager Mike LaMonica was also able to increase profit by reducing expenses. He saw that Shafter Lake had dwindled largely because of ARCO's massive layoff a few years earlier, in which much of the company's experience was dismissed. "When we took over, we could see how they had been wasting money. We got rid of automated equipment and went with a more human touch. The automation had saved manpower cost, but what they saved in manpower they lost in mechanical efficiency."

Cutting expenses was Mike's *forte*. He was adept at doing something with nothing: he could operate a field on a shoestring budget, and he demanded a discount on the shoestring. Bob Howard, Henry's wireline vendor from way back, paid Mike a great compliment. Sort of. "There's never been a person who was thriftier with Mr. Henry's money than Harold Meredith, except maybe for Mike LaMonica. He was extremely thrifty—you might even call him cheap!" Bob recalls one day reaching his limit with Mike's stinginess. "We were talking about a charge on a ticket, and I guess I had just had enough. And I finally looked at him and said, 'Mike, did you get out of bed this morning just to beat poor ol' Bob Howard out of a damn quarter?' And Mike started laughing and said, 'OK, I'll ease up.'"

Henry produced results almost immediately at Shafter Lake. Within a few months, total production, which had been declining at 700 BOPD, popped up to 1000, then flattened out at 800 and remained at that level.

The Shafter Lake MIP went on to yield significant financial profit for both ARCO and Henry, and the partnership also became a friendship that flourished in both oil deals and nonprofit work. Tony Best and Jim each served as United Way presidents and shared their time and resources with the Midland community. Later, when Henry was pioneering the Wolfberry play, and Tony landed at Pure Resources, the partnership became bountiful beyond imagining.

In late 1994, Dennis, in search of another MIP, was following on with his ARCO contacts. He was talking with Tom Holland, ARCO's VP of land, about building on the partners' successful Shafter Lake project. Tom suggested ARCO's Sho-Vel-Tum (SVT) property, in south-central Oklahoma, as a possible candidate.

SVT is an amalgam of multi-pay oil fields clustered around the Sholem, Velma and Tatums fields, discovered in the early 1900s. The main reservoirs at ARCO's holdings were the Springer Sands of Pennsylvanian age (slightly older than the Permian), which had cumulated more than 220 million barrels of oil and one trillion cubic feet of gas.

SVT is a very complex geological structure: it is the subsurface extension of the east-adjacent Arbuckle Mountains, and the strata have been intensely contorted by tectonic folding and faulting. The field is also complex operationally. Recall that a *secondary* recovery project, generally a waterflood, is conducted to sweep more oil from a reservoir than the reservoir could produce on its own energy during *primary* recovery. Yet secondary projects still leave much oil trapped in the reservoir's pore spaces. Consequently, in some special cases, a *tertiary* project (from the Latin word for *third*) is implemented to recover still more oil. One such method involves injecting CO_2 into the reservoir, in the same way that water is injected during a secondary project. But CO_2 has an added benefit: when pumped into the reservoir at high pressures, it mixes with the oil, which swells the oil and makes it less viscous. The oil is then more easily pushed through the reservoir toward producers. ARCO had one of SVT's sandstones under CO_2 recovery for several years, and other parts of the field appeared to have similar potential.

The companies were close to signing an agreement when ARCO abruptly decided to sell the field. "It was quite disappointing when Tom [Holland] called and said they were in the final stages of negotiating a purchase and sale agreement with a prospective buyer," Dennis remembered. "So all of our MIP work was put in the file, and with downtrodden sadness hanging heavy in the air after evaluating a complicated CO_2 flood in another state, we moved on to the next opportunity."

Several weeks later, early in 1995, the opportunity resurrected just as abruptly—with a significant twist. "I got a call from Tom," Dennis said, "that ARCO's upper management had approved the sale agreement all the way through the corporate office, but on the day when execution was required, the prospective buyer had backed out. He asked me if Henry would be interested in buying the field for $40 million outright, instead of doing the MIP trade." There were two conditions: Henry must agree to the exact terms of the PSA already approved by ARCO management, and Henry must make it happen within about two weeks. Dennis responded, "We'll get after it!"

He scrambled a meeting on January 11 with all hands on deck. Dave Feavel was assisted by George Olson for the geological assessment, and Van Temple by engineer Steve Guthrie, whom Van had picked off from Exxon two years earlier. Mike LaMonica brought his cost-saving superpowers to bear on the operational evaluation. And there was a newcomer on the assignment sheet: geophysicist Gary Pitts, Dennis's friend from Sunday school, had left Neste and was working in Midland for an East Texas-based family office. The family was divesting its oil assets, so Gary had called Dennis to see whether Henry wanted a shot at them. Knowing that Gary was about to sell himself out of a job, Dennis replied, "Why don't you come over here and buy something rather than selling all the time?"

To clarify, Gary's academic training is in geophysics, but his *raison d'être* is deal-making. Gary will buy, sell, swap, carry, farmout, join or drill-to-earn—whatever it takes to finalize a good deal and get wells in the ground. Joining his close friend as Henry's business development manager was an opportunity he would not let pass by. Gary accepted Dennis's offer, rolled up his sleeves and charged into the SVT fray.

Part of the fray, perhaps the biggest part, was figuring out how Henry Petroleum, a little ol' Spraberry driller in Midland Texas, could come up with $40 million to fund the acquisition. Henry needed a partner. A large partner. To that end, in his minutes memo from the January 11 meeting, Dennis penciled instructions to the engineers: "Coordinate final pkg preparation for SG's review."

"SG" denotes SG Interests, the investment entity of Lester Smith and Russell Gordy, two Houston oilmen and extreme philanthropists who had partnered in oil and benevolence since 1986. After receiving the buy-it-now call from Tom Holland, Dennis contacted SG. One week later, the SG team arrived at Henry's office for a review, and, after vetting the proposal, agreed to partner in the purchase. Having secured a partner and funding, Henry then inked the deal with ARCO.

(During this time, Henry's Bob Dimit had been in discussions with ARCO about a position as business manager. ARCO offered and Bob accepted, and so, as Bob said, "I was on the Henry side of the table for the SVT evaluation, but on the ARCO side when the agreement was signed.")

In the end, Henry kept about a quarter of the project, and SG and their investors took the rest. This was quite a financial commitment for Henry, not only the big purchase price, but also the significant amount of capital the team had forecasted for the field optimization work. Recall that Henry had struggled to pay half a million dollars for Moonlight a few years earlier. The SVT acquisition was proof that Jim and Dennis had stepped hard on the growth pedal.

Due to the complexity of the SVT project, Henry needed folks skilled in CO_2 floods, and they had none. For the field operations work, Mike and Dennis interviewed ARCO's staff and were fortunate to find two excellent superintendents, Randy Endicott and Bill Domstead, both of whom they hired. Back in Midland, Van and Dennis hired staff engineer Keith Maberry, who had solid experience working for Phillips Petroleum on its large CO_2 fields. Dennis also hired Ronnie Scott, then at Exxon, to be operations manager for Henry's "Midcontinent Division"—in other words, the SVT project. Ronnie would later become president of Henry and play a major role in the sale to Concho at the peak of the Wolfberry epic.

Soon after Henry assumed operations, a major dispute arose between Henry and Occidental Petroleum (Oxy) regarding the use of a CO_2 pipeline that Henry needed to supply its tertiary flood operations. Sparing all the litigant details, each of the two companies filed suit against the other. Both desired to settle their disputes outside of court. Dialogue proceeded, with Ronnie representing Henry's interests and talking regularly with his Oxy counterpart. A year later, the dialogue had not resolved anything, and relations between the company reps were becoming acrimonious. Ronnie and the Oxy man talked every night by phone. One night, when the discourse became particularly heated, Ronnie suddenly realized how badly they were both behaving. He calmed and asked his opponent, "Are you a Christian?" The man also calmed and responded, "Yes, I am." Ronnie replied, "Well, so am I. But you wouldn't know it. How about if we just go forward and behave as Christians?"

Within seven months the suits were settled, out of court and in an arrangement that benefitted both companies. Although he had been at Henry for less than a year, Ronnie had seen that this sort of goodwill, the win-win way of doing business, was Henry's standard. Recalling the turning point and resolution of the Oxy dispute, he said, "To me, that's Henry."

So Henry's Midcontinent Division—all five guys—went to work implementing their plans and addressing SVT's operational complexities. And the rest of the Henry team continued to scout for more MIPs.

The East Ackerly Dean Unit (EADU) in southeastern Dawson County comprises about 4800 acres and had been on waterflood recovery since the early 70s. The unit was operated by Conoco, and consisted in forty-four wells, drilled on 80-acre spacing (one well every 80 acres in a regular pattern, like trees in an orchard). In 1996, Bob Irelan was manager of exploration and production for Conoco's Midcontinent Region (which had many more than five people), and through his friendship with Jim at the United Way, he proposed a Henry-Conoco partnership at EADU. The Henry team assessed the existing waterflood performance, and recognized value in drilling additional wells between the existing wells (we call these *infill* wells) to recover more oil reserves from the unit.

Negotiations ensued, on a deadline. Mike LaMonica, Henry's operations manager who would be in charge of the drilling program, did not have time to peruse Conoco's mountain of files to see how they had designed their earlier drilling program. He made some low-cost assumptions, as was his routine, and arrived at a cost of $235,000 per well. At those costs, Van Temple's forecast of how much oil could be made indicated that the project would be marginally profitable, and the Henry team went forward with their proposal.

In the proposal pitched to Conoco, Henry would drill thirty-three infill wells, pay 100% of the drilling costs, and earn 40% interest in the unit. Conoco accepted. Henry then turned and offered 75% of its piece to SG Interests, the friends who had partnered with Henry at SVT. Based on the profit forecasted by Mike's quick and dirty cost estimates, SG joined with Henry.

Then there appeared an oops. With the hurry-up evaluation over, Mike was finally able to examine Conoco's files. He saw many *casing* leaks in the existing unit wells (casing is pipe cemented into a borehole to keep the hole stable and to protect shallow, water-bearing zones from oil being produced through the pipe). He realized that Henry's program would need an improved casing design—as in, more expensive. With the new costs, the project's already tread-water economics would be slightly submerged. After mulling the ramifications of his oops, Mike went to Dennis with a self-preserving solution: "I think Ronnie needs some Permian drilling experience."

Ronnie was given charge of the EADU project. Because of its size and the speed with which it had to be completed, he needed an expert drilling and completions superintendent assigned solely to the project. He knew the perfect guy to call. Ronnie had met Doug Smith a few years before, when both were at Exxon. At the time, Ronnie was an operations manager, calling shots from the office, and Doug was a field superintendent in charge of a workover program at one of Exxon's large waterfloods in Scurry County. Doug was not optimistic after their initial meeting: "When Ronnie left the field that day, I really thought there was no way I could ever work for this guy. But I soon found out that I didn't want to work for anyone else." Doug had twenty-five years of industry experience, fifteen with Exxon, and he was currently working with a small outfit. "I never had heard of Henry, didn't know who they were. Ronnie just called me out of the blue one night."

Doug joined Henry as a contract drilling foreman in September 1996. Ronnie assigned him to the new EADU project along with pumper Roy Madison, and the three men got busy. Seriously busy. Ronnie told them, "I'm going to work us all to death to get through this. It's going to be tough, but I'll make it right later."

They drilled and completed the thirty-three project wells between September 1996 and September 1997. For some of that time, they had three drilling rigs running simultaneously, which Doug superintended singlehandedly. And there were the forty-four existing wells to maintain, so Roy was running everywhere. "We were busy beyond belief," Doug said. "A two-man show in the field, just me and Roy. No way I can ever explain how truly remarkably busy we were. I used to say that Ronnie Scott couldn't dream up enough work that Roy and I couldn't handle it. I was almost wrong."

Actually, it wasn't a two-man show. There was also Roy's wife, Faye. "When Doug figured out she knew what to look for on my pumper's route, he would say, 'Can Faye come out and check your wells today and you help me run this casing?' And I'd say, 'Sure.' So she would come out in her pickup and drive around and check her lease." Notice that Roy called it "*her* lease."

As often happens in time of battle, Doug and Roy developed an enduring *esprit de corps* at EADU. To Roy, Doug is "more like a brother. I've got a saying: I can cuss him, but I'm gonna whip the other guy that does." For his part, Doug said, "I never met a man who worked so hard, always ready to help and please, as Roy. You didn't have to worry about whatever was assigned to Roy. It was going to be taken care of."

The team's hard work paid off. They had additional help in the office from Henry's recently hired quartermaster, Steve Owen. Among other skills, Steve is a procurement wizard, and he was able to scavenge used *pumping units* (or pump jacks—the things that look like rocking horses) from all over the country, to hold down costs on the new producers.

When the project dust settled—not literally, of course, the dust never settles in West Texas—the team had brought in the entire program right at the forecasted cost, notwithstanding Mike's low-ball. And the results were excellent. The production rate increased to 1500 BOPD from 600, then dropped back to 900 and remained flat for the next few years. Even with uncooperative oil pricing, the project was a success.

Bob Irelan exited Conoco in March 1998, half a year after Henry completed the project. He would be leaving Midland to join Oxy in the company's California headquarters. In his farewell interview with the *Midland Reporter Telegram*, he mentioned only one of his many successes while at Conoco: "One of the deals I am proud of is the deal with Henry Petroleum in which we allowed Henry to buy into a venture, add the value, operate it and participate in the returns." No longer was Henry Petroleum relying on its own reckoning of success, but major partners were affirming it.

At the time of his departure, Bob Irelan had been serving as president of the local United Way. To fill his post, the UW board approached Tony Best, Jim's friend and Henry's partner in the ARCO Shafter Lake MIP. But the same week that Bob Irelan announced his leaving Conoco—in fact, the day before—Tony announced that ARCO was transferring him south of the border, to serve as president of ARCO Latin America. The UW board defaulted instead to a recent past president: Jim Henry. Jim had first been elected president of the UW in 1994, after three years on the board of Casa de Amigos. Now the UW folks asked him, "Will you take over for the rest of Bob's term?" Jim was in a bit of a conundrum: "Paula was off on a trip, and I couldn't get hold of her. So I told them I would. Just about got a divorce—United Way takes a lot of time!"

———————

In early 1998, shortly after signing a small MIP with Pioneer at their Ackerly Dean Unit, next door to Conoco's EADU, Henry bagged the mother of all MIPs.

Mobil's colossal Pegasus-Parks Field in Midland and Upton Counties bore the same hopeful marks as Shafter Lake: discovered and initially developed in the 50s, production from the deep Ellenburger up through the shallow San Andres, and languishing production. Whereas ARCO's Shafter Lake property had only 70 wells, though, Pegasus-Parks had several hundred.

Dennis knew that if a MIP were to be made, he needed to initiate discussions with someone way up in Mobil's C-Suite. He had learned that lower-level minions tended to take the easy road and quash such opportunities with a quick no. Dennis went to the top. "I cold-called Mike Yeager, the president of Mobil Oil Corp in Dallas, and we visited on the phone about Henry Petroleum, our MIP track record, and what we had been able to accomplish on different fields. The words fell on fertile ground, and he was very intrigued by the idea."

Jim and Dennis flew to Dallas and presented Henry's proposal. Yeager liked what he saw, and directed his Midland manager, Jack Rathbone, to give Henry an audience. The talks progressed, and in October of that year the companies signed a preliminary agreement. They created two technical teams, Mobil's headed by Reggie Beasley and Henry's by Gary Pitts, Van Temple and Mike LaMonica. The teams agreed that Mobil would continue to operate the deep wells—the Ellenburger and Devonian producers—and Henry would assume operations of the shallower reservoirs—the Penn, Wolfcamp, Spraberry, Clearfork and San Andres (listed from older to younger, deep to shallow).

As with the Shafter Lake MIP, a baseline production forecast would be determined for the project. For the all-important task of establishing the forecast, Van tapped Mark Gully, a youngish engineer he had worked with at Union Texas. Mark had been at Henry for six years. "I did my due diligence on every well: when was it drilled, which zones had and had not been completed, what condition the wellbore was in, etc. Then I went to Mobil's office and discussed current producing rates and existing declines, wellbore integrity, and my projections for each of the production curves." Mark's Mobil counterparts accepted his forecasts with only slight modifications, and the deal foundation was laid. The MIP was signed on March 30, 1998, under the official name, The Pegasus-Parks Area Field Management and Enhancement Agreement—FMEA for short.

Given the size and importance of the project, Henry needed to add a few more staff. The MIP also presented a unique operational complexity: due to the depth-severed structure of the arrangement, with Mobil operating deep wells and Henry shallow wells within the same field, Henry's field personnel would be working right on top of Mobil's—literally. In fact, by the terms of the deal, some of Mobil's employees would be supervised by a Henry foreman. "When you've got two companies operating on the same real estate," Dennis noted, "with tank batteries side by side, with Mobil unionized employees operating their facility and with Henry Petroleum employees and contractors operating near them—that gave Mobil a lot of concern. How was the union going to take this, and how was Mobil going to be affected?"

And all of this in addition to the historic symbolism of the field: Pegasus was named for the company's winged red horse, its iconic symbol since the early 1930s when Mobil was operating as the Magnolia Petroleum Company.

Consequently, Henry's field superintendent for the project had to be a diplomat as well as an operations expert. Glyn Pace fit the bill perfectly. Ronnie had worked with Glyn at Exxon: "Glyn is one of the finest men I've ever known. The field back then was rough and coarse, but he was never that way. He is such a strong Christian man, someone you want to be like. I wanted to be like Glyn." Glyn was employed elsewhere at the time, but Ronnie tracked him down and hired him as the FMEA was being signed.

For stewarding the office responsibilities, Henry hired engineer

Terry Burkes, a Midlander and Texas Tech grad, with national and international experience working for Anadarko and Citation. Unlike many other Henry hires, Terry is not an instance of "it's who you know." "Being from Midland originally, I knew Henry had a great reputation, and I was looking for a position where I could work both reservoir and operations engineering. So I responded to an ad in the MRT." Terry impressed Ronnie during the interview and started on July 1, while the FMEA negotiations were ongoing. He began as a staff engineer and was later promoted to an FMEA management post.

Within the first twenty-four months of the project, Henry had spent more than $3 million conducting sixty workovers, mostly returning shut-in wells to production, performing recompletions, making repairs and optimizing pumping equipment. The team's efforts had tapped into 1.4 MMBO above what Mobil had captured to that point.

Most of the work was immediately profitable. But Henry did some work that lost money—intentionally. A few of the properties under Henry's care were already below the production baseline at the project's start, which meant that Henry would have to spend some profitless capital just to bring the producing rate up to the forecast. Terry suggested to Dennis that work on those properties be postponed, so the team could initially focus on profitable leases. "But Dennis quickly advised me, 'Don't worry about that. I want to work on all the properties, because that was the intent of the deal.' It was the right thing to do. Not to mention the importance of projecting Henry's integrity to Mobil by honoring our commitment over economics. So yes, we lost money on a couple projects. But within a year and a half, production was above baseline on all the properties."

In addition to making more oil, Henry profited by spending less money. Mike LaMonica had spotted all manner of operational inefficiency: "I spent a lot of time with the Mobil field people and learned a lot about what was going on. And I told Dennis, 'We can turn this thing around. We can make money just by saving operating costs alone.'" In short order, Mike worked his cost-cutting magic and dropped expenses by more than half.

The FMEA partnership between Henry and Mobil was extremely profitable for the two companies for a long time. Actually, the partnership was profitable for *four* companies. Exxon inherited the arrangement when it merged with Mobil in late 1999, and carried on with Henry still as operator. Then in 2008, Henry sold its interest to Concho Resources, who assumed operatorship and continued the program with ExxonMobil.

During the 90s, Henry's MIP projects succeeded in growing the company, not like a rocket, but steadily. Perhaps more importantly, the MIPs stabilized it, with their diverse types of work projects, high well counts and the strength of the major partners. All of this was made effective by the Henry team's competence in planning and executing the work. As Jim and Dennis had intended, the MIPs established for the company a much firmer foundation. In the latter part of the decade, with Henry's asset base now spread well beyond the Spraberry, they were free to consider changes to their business model that would not have been advisable in the past.

One summer day in 1996, as he was headed to the Phoenix Unit to run his route, Roy Madison got a call from Mike LaMonica. Mike asked where he was. "I'm on 137 outside Lenorah. Why?" "Don't go to the lease," Mike said. "Pull over and wait. I'll come to you." When Mike arrived, he started with, "I know we never sell properties, but we're about to make an exception."

One of the Phoenix Unit working interest owners—the bully, in fact—had accepted a buyout offer from Fort Worth oilman Duer Wagner. Oil was spiking to $22 from $16, and the unit's production was 250 BOPD and barely declining. Wagner's offer reflected both positives. Henry decided to tag along with the bully and *flip* (sell, exit the project) to Wagner. At the time, the team was closing the EADU MIP trade with Conoco, and they could use the proceeds to help fund that venture.

The reason that Henry "never sold properties" was that the operating fees charged to the partners on a per-well basis were essential to pay the company's overhead in the Spraberry business model. As a result, Henry wanted always to increase and preserve well count. But with this sale, the company was moving in the opposite direction. The Henry Version 2.0 deals—the Moonlight acquisition, Shafter Lake MIP and the Phoenix flood itself—were beginning to liberate the company from total dependence on the Spraberry. Of course, the Spraberry had made Henry successful, and it was still supplying excellent revenue. But the sale showed Henry's confidence that diversification efforts were gaining traction—the company was stabilizing and expanding, rather than merely sustaining itself.

Henry made additional divestments in the next few years. In late 1998, they sold the Moonlight property. The team had squeezed significant reserves out of the field since purchasing it nine years earlier, and total production was now marginal. Henry had recently signed its Mobil FMEA, and used the Moonlight proceeds to help fund the capital work.

A few years later, in December 2001, Henry sold SVT to Chaparral Energy. Henry had operated the property for seven years, and experienced tough going the whole time. Over the project's arduous life and including the sale, when all the accounting was done, Henry had made $10 million before tax.

More meaningful and lasting to the company were the staffing gains during the SVT venture, excellent employees who would stick around and help take the company to the next level. These included engineers Ronnie Scott and Keith Maberry in the office, and Randy Endicott in the field. Randy is cut from the same cloth as Glyn Pace. He was much too valuable a man to lose through the SVT sale, and Ronnie offered to move Randy from Oklahoma to Texas as the Shafter Lake field superintendent, and he accepted.

Henry had learned that there is a time for every purpose under Heaven, including a time to flip. As a result, strategic asset divestments became a part of the company's business model—not frequent, but familiar. And these early sales were mere warmups to the life-changing trio of sales that would begin five years later.

———————

Waterflood units had been all the rage in the Permian Basin during the 1950s and 60s. As fields discovered in the 20s and 30s were depleting from their primary pressure drives, operators routinely pooled their interests and implemented flood projects. Most of these floods were in porous carbonates on the Central Basin Platform, primarily in the Permian-aged Clearfork and San Andres, with some in the older Devonian and Penn reservoirs. Down in the basin, operators also put together a few waterflood units in the Spraberry sandstone.

There had been a general dearth of unitization projects since that heyday, as most of the fields with obvious flood potential were already being flooded. The remaining fields were either very small or of a lesser reservoir quality, and often not worth the effort and investment. But a few units were formed and flooded in the 80s, one of which was Henry's Phoenix Grayburg Unit in 1987. Phoenix had been wonderfully successful for Henry, not only financially but educationally: it had taught the company how to plan, unitize, implement and manage a waterflood. So during the 90s, as Henry began to diversify its assets base with MIPs, the company was particularly open to deals that included waterflood potential, which they found at Shafter Lake with ARCO and EADU with Conoco. They also looked for waterflood opportunities outside of MIP structures that Henry could acquire all or a portion of.

Because waterflooding is a distinct niche in the industry, and because Henry implemented several of them, their flood experiences warrant a separate thread. But keep in mind that this chronicle takes place concurrent with Henry's other MIP and flip activity.

In spring of 1991, Henry acquired some leases in the small Peacock Field in Stonewall County, on the Midland Basin's way-northeastern shelf. The field produces from the Tannehill Formation, a sandstone 20-feet thick at a depth of 3500 feet. Waterflood potential at Peacock, the team figured, could be about half as much as Phoenix. The investment would be low as the field would not require any new drilling, therefore the project ought to be profitable. Henry partnered with Neste (the Finnish national oil company with an office in Midland), and land manager Bill Fair and his staff rounded up the field's owners and created a unit agreement without issue—no bully this time. The team secured Railroad Commission approval in November 1992, and Mike LaMonica's operations group converted three oil-producing wells to water injectors and started the flood. But unlike the Phoenix flood, whose beautiful response enraptured Bob Dimit, the Peacock didn't fly. The sandstone turned out to be many separate, isolated reservoirs, and the injected water could not pass through the strata and push oil to the producers. Because the investment was small, there was little harm done, but little gain either, and Henry sold the field a few years later. Unlike Phoenix, the Peacock did not rise again. Which was just as well.

But Henry was not done flooding. Recall that the agreement with ARCO in the Shafter Lake MIP, signed a year after the Peacock project, required that Henry evaluate the Clearfork for the possibility of secondary recovery. Henry's technical team started work on that study as soon as the MIP was signed, and after more than a year of on-and-off evaluation, the team concluded that the Clearfork should flood with moderate success. They projected that by infilling the field to 20-acre spacing (that is, drilling new injection wells in between the existing 40-acre producing wells), the flood could recover close to 7 MMBO. Their economic forecast indicated a profit, so Henry moved ahead.

As with Phoenix and Peacock, all owners in the field would have to be brought together in a unit agreement. For that, land manager Bill Fair would need to add some solid help in his department. He called Gary Elander, a friend from his days contracting for Parker & Parsley, and asked for recommendations. Gary gave Bill a few names and wished him luck. But Gary was missing the point: "About a week later, Bill calls back and says that none of those candidates would work out and asks if I have any more ideas. I tell him those were my *A* picks, but I'll give it some more thought. Bill pauses and then says, 'Well, how about you?' I paused and then said, 'Yeah, how about me?!' I have never forgotten that special moment." Special for Henry, too, as Gary would later contribute meaningfully to the Wolfberry campaign.

Gary started the unitization effort on St. Patrick's Day, 1994, by notifying *University Lands* of Henry's intent. (University Lands manages surface and mineral interests for the Permanent University Fund, an endowment that supports both the University of Texas and Texas A&M's systems. Henry's planned flood included acreage stewarded by UL, and they needed approval.) The agreement was ratified by UL and the working and royalty owners in mid-fall, and RRC approval was granted in early December. The Shafter Lake Clearfork Unit (SLCU) was born.

Henry initiated the work early in 1995. The company had a lot going on at the time, as they were closing on SVT and trying to get folks hired for that project. Because of the complexities at SVT, Mike LaMonica gave that project his full attention and dished off the more sedate SLCU flood implementation to two of his reports, Mark Gully and Steve Guthrie. Both men identified the SLCU project as one of the most fulfilling in their careers. "Mark and I were pretty much left alone to conduct the infill drilling and waterflood startup,"

Steve said, "Pretty fun for a 10-year engineer!" And Mark explained that he worked on the unit "as both the field engineer and office engineer—lots of work but very fulfilling to see it come together." The pair drilled eleven injectors and three producers, and they did additional work on nineteen existing wells, to ensure that all were open and stimulated in the targeted pay zone. They also planned and installed the water injection distribution system.

By mid-summer, the project was ready for startup. To celebrate the occasion, Jim and Dennis decreed an on-site barbecue feast for startup day, July 24. In true Henry fashion, the company wanted to thank everyone who had assisted in the project, from top to bottom. They invited sixty-five people to the event—only nineteen were Henry employees, and the rest were vendors, contractors and service hands. Henry's field staff did not even know the names of some of the folks who had helped, but they wanted all to be at the party, so the official invitation list included "the 4-man roustabout crew" and "the oil pipeline gauger."

The new waterflood was a big deal not only for Henry, but for the whole community of Andrews. The *Midland Reporter Telegraph*'s oil editor, John Paul Pitts, was in attendance that day, and he described the project as "one of the largest and most significant waterfloods in Andrews County in recent years." (His article about the barbecue included a few pictures, one of which shows a man at a portable cook-out rig with the unsettling caption, "Bob Williamson of MI Drilling Fluids prepares a tasty barbecue lunch").

Jim opened the proceedings with greetings and thanks, then turned over the podium to Dennis. As Bob Howard, Henry's favored wireline man, recalled, "That was the first time I've ever been in the oil field where I saw a man give a prayer before we did something. And that was Dennis Johnson. Asking the Lord to bless our efforts and what we were doing. I was very impressed with that. A lot of guys talk the talk, but obviously Henry walks it, too."

Oil production at SLCU climbed steeply from the flood start.

Two years later, it had increased sevenfold, from 180 BOPD to almost 1400, higher by far than the field's primary peak of 850. The financial return was unfortunately dampened by sliding oil prices during 1997 and 1998, and the flood's post-peak oil decline was a bit steeper than anticipated. Nevertheless, it was on track to recover 3 MMBO—it was profitable, the cash flow was strong, and the project was just the diversifier that Henry needed.

With the successes at Phoenix, Shafter Lake and EADU, Henry was no longer viewed only as a Spraberry driller but a Permian Basin waterflood expert. One University Lands manager referred to Henry as "the waterflood kings." The company continued its search for properties with flood potential, both within MIP-type arrangements and as outright acquisitions. But there were very few opportunities remaining, and as the 90s drew to a close the pickings were slim indeed.

In early 1999, the team identified a flood candidate in south-central Andrews County, a postage stamp-sized acquisition target producing from the San Andres. The economic assessment was favorable, and they moved forward with the Henry Cowden Grayburg-San Andres Unit. The project made a profit in the end, despite recovering fewer reserves than anticipated, but the flood was too small to move Henry's needle in either direction. Later that year, Henry played peacemaker between two companies that each owned about half of the Homann San Andres Field in Gaines County. The two parties agreed that their small field should be waterflooded, but they could not settle on terms. It took Henry more than a year to coax the owners to a unitization agreement, and another six months to drill several wells, all for a 20% ownership in the project. The Homann San Andres Unit finally began injection in January 2001, and it was both technically and economically successful. But again, due to size, the project didn't add much to Henry's growth.

Still in 1999, while Henry's land department was mediating the Homann discussion, the team managed to ink a small MIP with Marathon at that company's Olson Field in Crockett County. The goal of the arrangement was for Henry to improve an existing San Andres waterflood. That project failed, but Olson is noteworthy in that it was the occasion for Henry's first ever horizontal well (more on that later).

In 2001, as the Homann flood began injection, Henry conducted what would be its final unitization project. In Henry's original discussions about the Shafter Lake MIP with ARCO, the San Andres reservoir had been discussed as a flood candidate, along with the Clearfork, but had been back-burnered due to the Clearfork's greater potential. Henry's technical team had later assessed the San Andres and concluded that a flood should be profitable on a small scale, so they formed the University San Andres Unit and commenced injection on November 1. Henry's results, both technical and economic, were not good—it is fortunate that the scale was small.

In August 2001, Henry landed an inconspicuous little MIP with Burlington Resources at the McCamey Field in western Upton County. The deal itself ultimately yielded no financial gain to the company whatsoever. In fact, Henry allowed the arrangement to lapse at the end of its initial eighteen-month term without spending a dime of capital. But the project led to a series of fortunate events that soon catapulted Henry to stardom.

The McCamey field is very old—producing since the 1920s—and very large: Burlington's portion included 200 wells that had made 135 MMBO. Some parts of the field had been flooded and others had not, and Burlington admitted to "poor well conditions (many unknown)...the project is a failure to-date." These complexities were the hallmarks of MIP potential, and Dennis assigned his ace engineer, Van Temple, to the case. Van was ill at the time and could use some help with the onerous project, but the other engineers were busy with other work.

Good Providence had already arranged assistance. At that same time, on a lake in East Texas, another ace engineer was second-guessing his early retirement from ARCO. He was a good friend of Dennis, and called him to ask whether Henry had any projects he could help with. This man's name is also Dennis, and—though no one could have seen it at the time—this other Dennis was the final cast member needed to begin production of Henry's soon-to-be-released blockbuster, *The Wolfberry Play*.

———————

Henry's program of MIPs, flips and floods had tremendously matured the company during the 1990s. By the dawning of the new century, Henry had established a reputation for waterflooding expertise alongside its Spraberry skill, and had earned the respect and trust of several major companies as a high-quality operating partner. The company was now firmly supported by a diverse array of project types, and its fair market value had more than tripled, to about $20 million. Although Henry has not conducted any waterflood projects since then, it has very successfully continued MIPs and strategic flips to the present, and we will encounter several of each later in the book.

Before the Wolfberry curtain comes up, we will pull over for another technical short course. The engineering technique of *hydraulic fracturing* is about to become very important in the Henry plot. That technique has been clouded in misinformation, misrepresented and unfairly villainized by folks who do not understand it. We will spend a few pages dispelling that cloud, so that the great Henry story may continue in clarity.

They've only just begun: Paula and Jim Henry in Midland in 1970, shortly after founding the oil company.

Jim (standing) and Bob Landenberger posing for the Midland Reporter Telegram as H&L Consultants, early 1970.

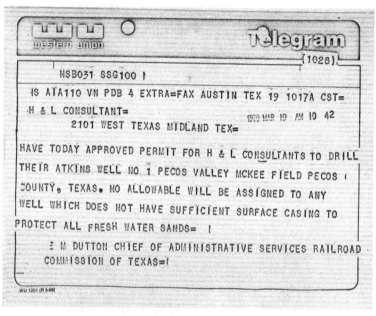

Railroad Commission approval to spud the Atkins #1, the first well drilled by H&L (Hanson Oil Corp was the operator of record).

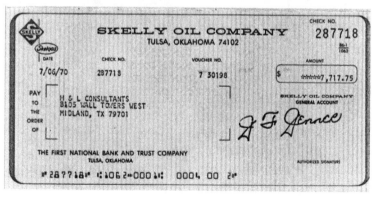

Skelly's payment to H&L for their Martin County Spraberry study.

H & L CONSULTANTS
B105 WALL TOWERS WEST
MIDLAND, TEXAS 79701
AC 915 682-9491

JIM HENRY
RES. 694-8398

BOB LANDENBERGER
RES. 694-6784

Henry & Landenberger Inc.
OIL & GAS OPERATORS

105-B Wall Towers West
Midland, Texas 79701

James C. (Jim) Henry
President

Office 915/682-9491
Res.   915/683-6716

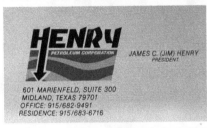

HENRY
PETROLEUM CORPORATION

JAMES C. (JIM) HENRY
PRESIDENT

601 MARIENFELD, SUITE 300
MIDLAND, TEXAS 79701
OFFICE: 915/682-9491
RESIDENCE: 915/683-6716

HENRY PETROLEUM BUILDING
3525 ANDREWS HIGHWAY
MIDLAND   TEXAS   79703
9 1 5 / 6 9 4 . 3 0 0 0
FAX 915/694.2999

JAMES C. (JIM) HENRY
President

HENRY
PETROLEUM
CORPORATION

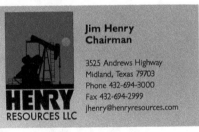

HENRY
RESOURCES LLC

**Jim Henry
Chairman**

3525 Andrews Highway
Midland, Texas 79703
Phone 432-694-3000
Fax 432-694-2999
jhenry@henryresources.com

A sampling of Jim's business cards
documenting the company's incarnations:
1970, 1973, 1981, 1991, and 2012

Jim with his good friends: above, Gene Sledge (R) in 1975, and below, Gene (R) and Bob Landenberger (L) in 2009.

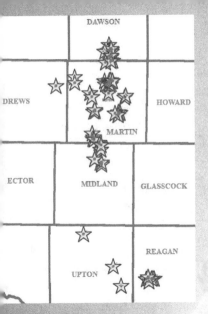

map showing the locations of Henry & Landenberger's 89 drilled wells.

Birth of the Phoenix: the blowout at the Parham #1, December 1971; the drilling rig is already melted to the ground on the right.

OG-10.
Rev. - 9-71

STATE OF WEST VIRGINIA
DEPARTMENT OF MINES

Oil and Gas Division

WELL RECORD

Quadrangle Ellenboro

Permit No. 47-073-1247

Rotary X   Oil _____
Cable _____   Gas X
Recycling _____   Comb. _____
Water Flood _____   Storage _____
Disposal _____
(Kind)

Company Henry Petroleum Corporation
Address 601 N. Marienfeld, Suite 300, Midland, Tx.
Farm A. M. Cunningham   Acres 138.21
Location (waters) _____
Well No. Two (2)   Elev. 860 GR
District Lafayette   County Pleasants
The surface of tract is owned in fee by
A. M. Cunningham, Rt. 1
Address Box H-29, St. Marys, W. Va. 26170
Mineral rights are owned by A. M. Cunningham
_____ Address as above
Drilling Commenced 7-15-81
Drilling Completed 7-20-81
Initial open flow 70 cu. ft. _____ bbls.
Final production 45 cu. ft. per day _____ bbls.
Well open 24 hrs. before test _____ R.P.
Well treatment details:

Casing and Tubing Size	Used in Drilling	Left in Well	Cement fill up Cu. ft. (Sks.)
20-16			
Cond.			
13-10"	30'	30'	-
9 5/8			
8 5/8	1110'	1110'	250
7			
5 1/2			
4 1/2		5297'	700
3			
2		4833'	-
Liners Used	-	-	-

Attach copy of cementing record.

Perforated 3337-4884' (43 shots). Fraced w/73,500# sand & 948 bbls wtr in foam.

Coal was encountered at _____ Feet _____ Inches
Fresh water _____ Feet _____ Salt Water _____ Feet _____
Producing Sand _____ Depth _____

Completion record for Henry Petroleum's Cunningham #2,
drilled far afield in Pleasants County, West Virginia, in 1981.

Henry Petroleum's office at 601 Marienfeld, "the Belgian waffle."

Above, Harold Meredith in his butt-chewin' prime, ca 1985, and left, at his retirement party in June 2002, with Dennis Johnson (L) and Mike LaMonica.

Below, Henry's executive officers back in the day: Buddy Martin (L) and Pete Peterson, ca 1990.

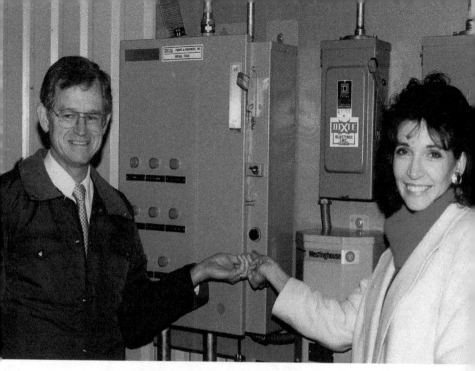

Above, Jim and Paula prepare to throw the switch at the Phoenix Grayburg Unit waterflood start-up, January 1988. Below, A plot of Phoenix Grayburg Unit oil production resulting from Henry's waterflood project.

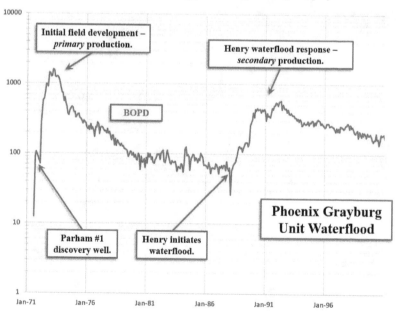

Initial field development – *primary* production.

Henry waterflood response – *secondary* production.

BOPD

Parham #1 discovery well.

Henry initiates waterflood.

Phoenix Grayburg Unit Waterflood

The face of Henry Petroleum in 1989: above, Dennis Johnson (L) and Jim (R), and left, their managers (L-R): Van Temple (engineering), Mike LaMonica (operations), Dave Feavel (exploration), Jay Bowden (finance), and Kaye Morelock (land).

Henry purchased this building at 3525 Andrews Highway in 1991, and the company resides there still today (picture taken in 2017).

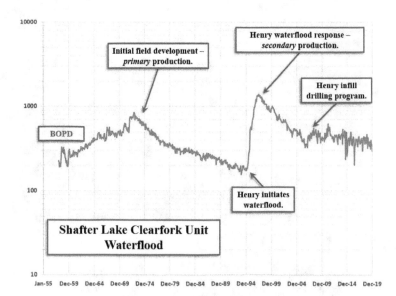

*A plot of Shafter Lake Clearfork Unit oil production
resulting from Henry's waterflood project.*

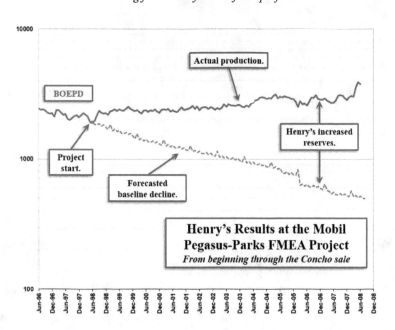

*A plot of oil production at the Pegasus-Parks FMEA Project with
Mobil, showing Henry's success in "bending the curve."*

The face of Henry Petroleum in 2001: Dennis and Jim seated in front;
behind them (L-R): Ronnie Scott (engineering), Dave Feavel (exploration),
Jay Bowden (finance), Gary Pitts (business development), Kim Harris
(finance), Bill Fair (land), and Mike LaMonica (operations).

Dennis Phelps, retired in East Texas in 2020, with the 2004 model F-150
he bought to service his Wolfberry wellsite frac work. Both are still going
strong: Dennis at 70-something years and the truck at 280,000 miles.

The two wells that birthed the Wolfberry: above, the pumping
unit on the Caitlin #2801, and below, Jim at the Beverly
tank battery with the #1 well pumping in the background.

RAILROAD COMMISSION OF TEXAS
OIL AND GAS DIVISION

OIL AND GAS DOCKET NOS. 125 & 126

Nos. 7 & 8 - 25,148

IN RE: CONSERVATION AND PREVENTION OF
WASTE OF CRUDE PETROLEUM AND
NATURAL GAS IN RAILROAD COM-
MISSION DISTRICTS NOS. 7-C AND
8, TEXAS

Austin, Texas
December 22, 1952

SPECIAL ORDER
COMBINING THE SEVERAL FIELDS PRODUCING FROM THE
SPRABERRY FORMATION IN THE TREND AREA, AND DESIGNATING
THE COMBINED AREA AS THE SPRABERRY TREND AREA FIELD,
MIDLAND, GLASSCOCK, REAGAN, UPTON, AND MARTIN COUNTIES, TEXAS.

WHEREAS, After due notice, the Railroad Commission of Texas held a hearing
September 11 - 17, 1952, for the purpose of considering rule changes for the
drilling and development operations within the area commonly known as the
Spraberry Trend Area; and

WHEREAS, From evidence adduced at said hearing, and from information gathered
from Commission records and investigations it is apparent that the Aldwell Spraberry, Benedum Spraberry, Pembrook, Pembrook North Spraberry, Weddell Spraberry,
Weiner Floyd Spraberry Fields all located in Commission District 7-C, and the
Midkiff, Driver Spraberry Sand, Tex Harvey (Floyd Sand) and Germania Fields,
all located in Commission District 8, are all producing from a common source
of supply or reservoir; that the Spraberry formation found productive in the

1952 Railroad Commission order establishing the STA Field.

*Permian Basin haute couture in 2004: the jacket
designed by Gary Pitts for his spec-ops team.*

135

Doug Smith training for wild Wolfberry wells in his college days, and now happily retired at his lake house in 2020.

Left, Bob Howard, Henry's long-time friend and wireline service provider, now retired and showcasing his world-class mineral collection in 2021.

The surprise party in February 2006, where Dennis Johnson announced his departure to found Summit Petroleum (L-R): Matt Johnson, Dennis Johnson, yours truly, and Ronnie Scott.

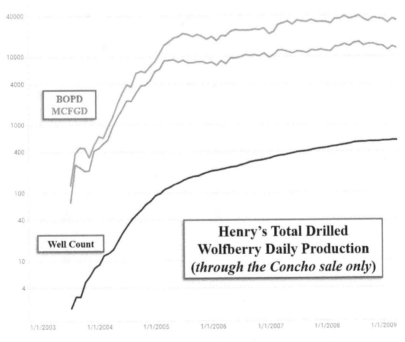

A plot of Henry's Wolfberry well count and daily oil and gas production up to the date of the sale to Concho.

Inking the sale of Henry Petroleum to Concho Resources in June 2008: Concho chairman and CEO Tim Leach with Paula and Jim.

Jim and Paula papering the sale of Henry Resources's assets to Linn Energy, with Mark Ellis, Linn's President and CEO, in May 2010.

Giving back: Paula and Jim present local non-profit Casa de Amigos with a gift from their personal coffer in October 2008; also pictured are CDA executive director Lael Cordes-Pitts (later to head the Henry Foundation) and Norbert Dickman, general manager of Fasken Oil & Ranch and president of the Casa de Amigos Endowment Board.

Henry's stalwart vertical Wolfberry rig, Savanna #605 (originally Lakota #42), seen here in 2010 drilling on the Robbie lease, just northwest of Midland's Loop 250 (note the city water tower in the background).

The Chevron-Henry partnership rides again at the signing of the BITS agreement, July 2013 (L-R): Chevron's team leader Bob Heimke and land advisor Charlie Ice, with Henry's exploration manager Craig Corbett and business development manager David Bledsoe.

Jim and Paula on location at the Sarah #1 horizontal well drillsite, October 2001.

Frac job underway on the Bohannon36 #1, Henry's first horizontal Wolfberry well, February 2014: panorama of the jobsite, and Jim monitoring events in the control van.

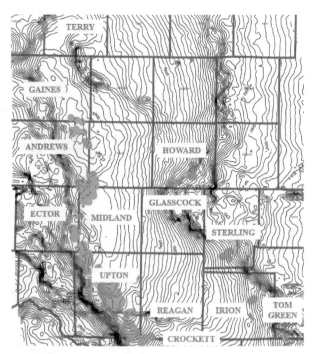

A map showing the locations of Henry's 45 Wolfberry prospects; the contours depict the subsurface topography of the Wolfcamp Formation (contour interval is 100 feet).

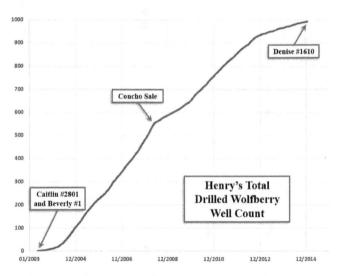

A plot of Henry's vertical Wolfberry drillwell count: the total is 992.

Roy Madison with Jim at a Henry frac pond (water storage facility) at the horizontal Trinity Prospect, in August 2015.

Henry going sideways: two contracted rigs drilling at Henry's reborn Phoenix prospect in central Upton County, June 2021. The rigs are situated about 1000 feet apart (angling leftward into the picture) drilling seven wells between them. Each borehole will go vertically downward to the Wolfcamp at about 9000 feet, then rotate to the horizontal and drill north (angling rightward into the picture) for two miles. The seven parallel laterals will be spaced about 500 feet apart and will collectively drain about 800 acres.

*Paula and Jim celebrating the 50th anniversary of
their oil company, November 1, 2019.*

*My handlers for this book project, who also play much more significant roles
at Henry (L-R): David Bledsoe, manager of the oil company, DiAnn Barker,
Jim's executive assistant, and Danny Campbell, manager of the investments.*

*Current members of Henry's field team (L-R): operations manager Billy
Bledsoe, Henry's long-time pulling unit contractor Victor Jordan, and three
veterans of the executive office: Claudio Lenisa, John Beckett and Roy Bray.*

*Some of the next-genners taking Henry into the future; front (L-R): marketing
analyst Rebecca Wilson, engineering technician Lindsay Dickson, chief investment
officer Misty Clary, and business development manager Patrick Cohorn; looming
in back—with the best hair in the company—is lift technician Brent Madison.*

The entire Henry crew, May 2021.

*Henry Resources's icon in 2021: celebrating the
past and looking forward to the future.*

Chapter 8
What Is a Frac?

HYDRAULIC FRACTURING IS the proper name of a method used to stimulate various types of oil and gas reservoirs, to enable them to produce their stores of hydrocarbons. The technique was pioneered almost a century ago and has been popularly used around the world for more than seventy years. Yet some contemporary opponents of the oil industry have selected fracturing as their point of attack, and have flooded the culture with accusations and misinformation, whether out of willful deceit or sincere ignorance.

I've written this chapter to provide a basic understanding of hydraulic fracturing, because the technique is essential to Henry's Wolfberry epic. The technical information and historical account are accurate, and I have tried to make them interesting. I have not at all written the chapter as an answer to opponents, but if any of the sincere variety read it, it should at least enable them to argue from an informed perspective.

Formation Stimulation

Completion

Picture a wellbore that has been drilled into a porous oil reservoir with some degree of permeability. Thirty-foot lengths of pipe, called *casing*, are then screwed together and lowered into the hole. The outside diameter of the casing is a little less than the diameter of the borehole, and the cylinder of space between the casing and the wall of the hole is called the *annulus*. Liquid cement is pumped down the casing, out the bottom and up into the annulus, and then allowed to harden. The cemented casing stabilizes the borehole for long use, and it protects any overlying fresh water-bearing strata from being contaminated by the oil as it moves up the inside of the casing.

The well is now ready for *completion*, the procedure for initiating production from the formation. First, a tool called a *perforating gun* is lowered into the hole to the depth of the reservoir. It isn't really a gun, and it doesn't shoot bullets. Rather, it is loaded with *shaped charges*, about an inch in diameter, that tightly focus the energy from the explosion through the casing. Each of these charges blows a nickel-sized hole in the pipe and creates a miniature tunnel a few feet out into the formation.

The reservoir is now open to the wellbore. At this point, some formations will *kick off* and flow without further prompting. We call this situation a *natural* completion: the reservoir's existing pressure and permeability are sufficient to push oil into the wellbore without man-made assistance. Examples of natural completion include the legendary gushers of yore, such as the 1901 Spindletop discovery in Beaumont and Shell's Barroso well in Venezuela in 1922, both of which flowed at the stratospheric rate of about 100,000 BOPD. In 1930, Dad Joiner's Daisy Bradford #3 in East Texas came in at a more conceivable rate of 300 BOPD. The Santa Rita #1, the 1923 Permian Basin discovery a dozen miles west of the town of Big Lake, came in naturally, too, but very manageably at 100 BOPD. Actually, the majority of natural completions of that era were relatively docile.

Most of the world's high-pressure, high-permeability fields have been discovered and developed, and almost all of today's reservoirs—shales in particular—do not produce naturally but require some form of *stimulation*.

Stimulation Options

Although there are many reasons why a reservoir might not flow on its own, I will focus only on low permeability. Recall that permeability is a measure of how easily fluids can move between the layer's pore spaces.

There are two primary causes of insufficient perm. In some cases, the *near-wellbore region*—that is, the cylinder of rock extending a few feet outward from the wellbore—has become plugged with debris from the drilling. If the rest of the reservoir has sufficient perm, the cure is to pump a solution of water and hydrochloric acid, HCl, into the formation in relatively small volumes to dissolve the drilling debris. This procedure is called a *clean-up acid job*.

In other cases, the reservoir itself has low permeability. In limestone reservoirs, a procedure called a *matrix acid job* is used to dissolve some of the actual rock, to widen the pore throats. (*Matrix* refers to the pervasive fabric of the reservoir—the rock and its pore network.) Matrix acidizing is performed primarily in limestones because calcite, the primary mineral in limestone, is easily dissolved by HCl. In matrix jobs, more acid is pumped in and reaches between ten and thirty feet out into the reservoir.

But a clastic reservoir (remember: sandstones, siltstones and shales) with low perm presents a problem. Acidizing does not generally work on clastics because the rock's grains are predominantly composed of silicate minerals, such as *quartz* (silicon dioxide,

SiO_2), which are not soluble in HCl. In the early days, drillers simply skipped over the low-perm clastics because there were plenty of high-perm formations available. But when the gushers were discovered and produced, the industry had to learn to stimulate low matrix perm in clastics some other way. And for the past seventy years, the technique of choice has been to induce artificial fractures in the rock by pumping in water at very high pressures.

This process is called *hydraulic fracturing*.

A Brief History of Fracking

The (Not So) Good Ol' Days

Not long after Edwin Drake started the oil industry by drilling the first oil well, in Titusville, Pennsylvania in 1859, drillers realized that most oil reservoirs need some form of stimulation. This need applied to existing producers that became plugged off with paraffin or debris, as well as new wells that had low perm or pressure (or both) to begin with.

At the time, it seemed reasonable to explode something in the borehole to shatter the reservoir and thereby improve its perm. After all, blasting had been used for two centuries in the mining industry (and still is today). I need to mention that most of these early wells were *open-hole completions*: the casing was not set on bottom but landed somewhere above the pay zone, which was left exposed to the blast in the wellbore. Gunpowder was the first explosive to be used. It was lowered into the hole and detonated across from the pay zone, in a process known as "shooting a well."

Nitroglycerin soon supplanted gunpowder, as it provided much more bang for the buck. Nitro was very effective. It was also very exciting, in a very bad way: because of its extreme instability, mishaps were routine and particularly gruesome.

And yet, nitro was still employed in parts of the US until just a few decades ago, long after better methods had been devised. In

Appalachia into the 1990s, there was still a handful of mom-and-pop nitro shops, both manufacturers and shooters. The life cycle of these businesses was clearly defined: each one kept at it until their manufacturing facility detonated or their last crew exploded, then they knew it was time to transition to a different business.

Craig Corbett, later to join Henry as exploration manager in 2008, provided a case in point. Craig cut his teeth in West Virginia in the late 70s with an outfit that performed drilling and completion work with its own equipment. When he started, the company had both nitro and dynamite in its stimulation arsenal. Craig said he never actually witnessed a nitro frac. Good thing, too: "They did shoot wells with nitro, but I never saw that happen. I did see a thirty-foot crater in a two-lane road where one of their trucks blew up and killed two people. That was in late 1977. From that point forward, they never did a nitro shot again." A clearly defined conclusion—time to transition.

Craig was, however, present at some dynamite fracs, and his comparison puts the hazards of nitro into even greater graphic relief: "We used to stack four-inch-diameter, twenty-foot-long sticks of dynamite in the open wellbore, usually three to four thousand feet of them. The giant sticks of dynamite were dangerous too, but much safer than nitro!"

There had to be a better way.

The Serendipitous Birth of Hydraulic Fracturing

Acidizing had been around since the beginning of the oil industry, but because it reacts with iron in the steel *tubulars* (the casing and production tubing in the wellbore), acid initially had only limited use, even in carbonate reservoirs.

In the early 1930s, a researcher made a significant breakthrough. Dr. Sylvia Stoesser was the first woman to be employed as a chemist by The Dow Chemical Company. She was put to work developing corrosion inhibitors that would allow acid to be safely used in well stimulation. Stoesser concocted organic inhibitors that protected the steel, and she created other fluid additives that broadened acid's usage.

With her supervisor, Dr. Hans Josef Grebe, Stoesser published a paper in the August 1935 edition of *World Petroleum* magazine, on acidizing applications made possible by her additives. The paper was titled "Increasing Crude Production 20,000,000 Bbl. From Existing Fields." While the article is a survey of a lot of acid work, it is also a major advertisement for Dow's recently created (1932) oil field subsidiary, Dow Well Service, later shortened to Dowell Inc., later to partner with Schlumberger. The article is fascinating from an historical perspective, as it gives a glimpse of the industry before petroleum engineering was a formalized discipline. And it includes a photo of the Dow field station in Midland, with acid trucks lined up and ready to service wells. The caption specifies that the location of the photo is "Midland, Texas," which was necessary to prevent readers from mistakenly assuming that it was the site of Stoesser's experiments at Dow headquarters in Midland, *Michigan*.

The article affirms that Stoesser had had great success with acid inhibition. But in her experiments, she had noticed something else that would prove to be of much greater moment. Dow used very salty, mineral-rich groundwater, called *brine*, to source chemicals for use in its business and lab experiments. The company produced the brine from shallow wells drilled at its facility, and returned the filtered water to the subsurface through shallow injection (or *disposal*) wells. Stoesser had done her acid job experimenting on these service wells. Toward the end of her article, she remarked about something that occurred inadvertently during the jobs:

> In the experiments on treating wells with acid for the production and disposal of brine for the Dow Chemical Company, it was discovered that a fluid pressure at the bottom of the

*well sufficient to counterbalance the weight of the rock above
it plus an additional pressure required for actually breaking
(cracking) the formation, makes possible the introduction of
fluids into new crevices thus created.*

When she pumped her fluid at pressures exceeding the weight
of the overlying strata (called the *overburden*), the rock actually
parted, or as she said, it "cracked." Stoesser was describing what
we now know as *hydraulic fractures*, narrow cracks only a few millimeters wide, created by pumping fluid at high pressure against
a formation exposed in a wellbore. She suggested that the chief
benefit of this "cracking" process was using the crack to pump acid
in higher volumes and into a larger area than could be achieved by
a matrix or near-wellbore job.

Note that Stoesser believed her fractures formed *horizontally*,
like a pancake: "High pressure hydraulic acid pumps...are capable
of producing sufficient pressure to force acid into newly made
cracks, *while the earth is compressed and even lifted*" [emphasis
mine]. Dow's service wells were very shallow, only a few hundred
feet deep, and therefore the overburden was not heavy in relative
terms. So she was probably correct on this heading. In any case,
her wording gave birth to the term *lifting pressure*, which operators
used to describe the pressure at which the overburden was lifted
and the formation parted.

Stoesser's thinking about fractures developing horizontally did
lead her to make one errant assumption of note. In discussing
deeper, low-perm reservoirs, she affirmed the then-popular recommendation that such rocks should "...be given a shot with an
explosive before acidizing in an attempt to crack the formation,
particularly when *the depth of the pay is such that it would be quite
out of the question to obtain sufficient pressure to distort the earth*"
[again, emphasis mine]. In other words, she assumed that all pres-
sure-created cracks were oriented horizontally, and therefore the

overburden must be lifted in every case. And because some reservoir depths are so great that no pump imaginable could perform the Atlassian feat of lifting such overburden, she reasoned that these reservoirs could not be cracked using her method. Stoesser was later proved wrong on this heading. But she gets a pass—a gold star, actually—because she was neither an earth scientist nor a petro industry insider, but a chemist trying to solve pipe corrosion issues. Yet she introduced a reservoir stimulation method that moved the industry forward an exceedingly long stride.

Stoesser described her method as "breaking," "cracking," "distorting" and even "rock busting," and though she referred to the equipment as "hydraulic acid pumps," she did not actually coin the phrase *hydraulic fracturing*. But this is really what she was promoting. True, the cracking phenomenon had been noticed by practitioners in acid and other pumping operations, such as cementing casing into wellbores. But Stoesser was the first to document its occurrence and, most important, to speculate on the benefits of intentionally inducing fractures this way.

After she and her husband had a daughter in 1940, Sylvia stopped working full-time for Dow. And so it turns out that the "Father of Fracking" is actually a mother, PhD chemist Sylvia Stoesser.

Fracking Comes of Age

Stoesser's work focused on acid treatment of limestones, but the petroleum world quickly realized that her serendipitous fracturing process should break any reservoir, whatever the rock type. Here at last was a method that could be employed in stimulating low-perm clastic reservoirs. And the new method of hydraulic fracturing was much safer than explosives—all of the crack and none of the boom.

Experimentation with the process was soon underway in various quarters. In the mid-1940s, two research engineers at Stanolind

Oil and Gas Corporation, Floyd Farris and Bob Fast, began testing the method systematically and on a large scale. From 1946 to 1948, they performed a collection of thirty-two fracs on twenty-three wells in five different states and several different formations. I need to point out that the Stanolind men, like Stoesser, experimented only on wells that were already producing and not on wells newly drilled. But their method, as with hers, could be applied to new wells also.

Fast and Farris presented their results at a 1948 AIME meeting in Dallas (the American Institute of Mining Engineers—*petroleum* engineering still wasn't a thing). Their Stanolind colleague, J. B. Clark, then published a report of their results in the January 1949 issue of *Petroleum Transactions of AIME*. The report is titled "A Hydraulic Process for Increasing the Productivity of Wells." Because of its historical significance, the paper is worth quoting at length.

Clark opens by explaining that "a process is being developed whereby the producing formation permeability is increased by hydraulically fracturing the formation." The process, which the team called "Hydrafrac"—note that the original, and therefore authoritative, spelling ends with a *c*—consisted in two steps. In Clark's words:

> *(1) injecting a viscous liquid containing a granular material, such as sand for a propping agent, under high hydraulic pressure to fracture the formation; (2) causing the liquid to change from a high to a low viscosity so that it may be readily displaced from the formation.*

Clark then lays out six primary requirements for the process. The fluid must be "oily," either gasoline or crude, rather than water-based, because fresh water swells the clay minerals in many clastic reservoirs, and consequently decreases perm. But he also suggests that, with more research, a way may be found to use water.

The fluid must also be pumped in at a high rate, and must be "sufficiently viscous that it can be injected into the well at pressure high enough to cause fracturing." If the fluid were too thin and pumped too slowly, it might move right through the formation's porosity network without cracking it. To increase the viscosity of their fluid, the team mixed it with a combination of *na*phthenic and *palm*itic acid—yes, that's *napalm*—which thickened, or *gelled*, the liquid, something like mixing flour in water to make gravy. Explosive gravy.

Also, the fluid "should carry in suspension a propping agent, such as sand, so that once a fracture is formed, it will be prevented from closing off and the fracture created will remain to serve as a flow channel for oil and gas." Acid etches the walls of a fracture in limestone and thereby prevents it from closing snugly. Acid does not affect most sandstones this way, but sand pumped into the crack would achieve the desired effect by *propping* the fracture open after pumping ceased. By adding proppant to the recipe, the Stanolind team formulated a universal treatment that would work on sandstones as well as carbonates.

After the fracture is created, Clark asserts, the fluid "must be thin enough to flow back out of the well and not stay in place and plug the crack which it has formed." To satisfy this requirement, the team pumped a volume of *breaker* (a chemical that breaks apart gelled molecules) behind the gelled frac fluid, which would reduce the fluid's viscosity to its normal level once all of it was in the reservoir.

Finally, Dr. Clark suggests that packers will be necessary in order to frac multiple intervals in a reservoir too thick to treat in a single event. (Even at this early time, engineers anticipated the need to frac multiple *stages*—separate pumping events at different depths in the wellbore—in a single completion; *stage fracking* is a necessary and standard procedure in today's horizontal development.)

Clark concludes with a discussion of the team's results: out of the thirty-two fracs, eleven resulted in a sustained increase in production, and there were valid reasons to explain away most of the unsuccessful jobs.

The US government issued the Stanolind team a patent in 1949 for the process of hydraulic fracturing. Stanolind promptly sold an exclusive license to HOWCO, the Halliburton Oil Well Company, which performed the first two commercial hydraulic fracturing treatments that same year, one in Stephens County, Oklahoma and the other in Archer County, Texas.

Hydraulic fracturing quickly became the stimulation method of choice. Some 300 wells were fracked in the first year, and by the mid-1950s the industry was averaging more than 3000 fracs per month. It was this new technique that facilitated the early Spraberry boom described previously.

Fracking Matures

As the patented Hydrafracs became routine, everyone assumed that the pumping pressure lifted the overburden and parted the formation along a horizontal plane, creating a flat, pancake-like fracture as Stoesser had believed. As operators began testing the process on deeper reservoirs, however, they found they could often fracture the zone with pump pressures significantly less than the calculated mass of the rock above. How was that possible?

In 1957, two researchers at Shell published a technical paper that answered the question. Using geophysical experiments and calculations, M. K. Hubbert and D. G. Willis demonstrated that hydraulic fractures will have a *vertical* orientation in what they called "tectonically relaxed" areas, and a *horizontal* orientation in areas of "tectonic compression." And they concluded that "in most cases, fracturing should be possible with pressure less than that of the overburden and, moreover, such fractures should be *vertical* [emphasis mine]." So, except in very shallow wells and wells drilled around active mountain-building (i.e., areas of tectonic compression), hydraulic fracturing produces fractures oriented vertically—up and down like a curtain rather than horizontally like a pancake. This improved understanding emboldened operators to conduct fracture stimulations on formations much deeper than had previously been thought possible.

(And by the way, the author of the paper, M. K. Hubbert, is the same King Hubbert of "peak oil" fame. In the same year that he published his fracture paper (1956), he made a presentation at the American Petroleum Institute convention in San Antonio, in which he predicted that US oil production would peak in 1965–70 and decline from that point. He was way wrong—should have stuck to fracture orientation.)

Quartz sand continued to be used as proppant in fracturing. It was not only plentiful and cheap, but it was natural. And since sand is simply eroded pieces of preexisting rock, fracking is basically putting sand back where it came from.

On the heels of Stanolind's published results, experimenters began using water as the hydraulic fracking fluid in place of crude and gasoline. When treated with a clay-stabilizing chemical, water turned out not to be so damaging. And because it was cheap, safe and easy to handle, water soon displaced oil.

As for gelling agents, while crews loved the smell of a napalm frac in the morning, it was neither cheap to acquire nor easy to handle and, most importantly, it didn't work in water. *Guar* was soon adopted as the go-to gelling agent. Guar is a legume, a bean cultivated for centuries in southern Asia as food for humans and cattle, now often used in the food industry as a thickener in dough, cheese and ice cream. Guar thickens water when mixed with it, forming another kind of gravy—non-explosive in this case.

Guar-gelled water is sufficient to carry enough sand to achieve what was thought to be the ideal proppant pack: a one-grain-thick coating of sand patchily spread across the fracture surface. Such packing, called a *partial monolayer*, is analogous to the crawlspace under a pier-and-beam house, where the crawlspace represents the fracture and the piers are individual grains, holding the fracture open (of course a fracture is vertical, not horizontal like a crawl-space). Such a pack has a relatively low cost because it requires minimal proppant, and it's highly permeable because the fluid flowing through the fracture is largely unimpeded by sand grains.

But in time the thinking changed, and folks came to favor coarser sand, more densely packed in the fracture. Proceeding on this assumption that *if a little is good, then mo' is better*, the industry went to work developing fluid thickeners capable of transporting higher concentrations of sand. In the early 1960s, an ARCO chemist was awarded a patent for a guar *cross-linker*, an agent that joins guar molecules together to form even longer chains, thereby increasing viscosity to transport higher sand concentrations.

Some additional ingredients were added to improve the overall process—for example, *friction reducer*, which makes the water *slick* so that it can be pumped more rapidly down the casing. *Biocide*, often basically bleach, was introduced to prevent casing-eating bacteria from growing inside the wellbore. *Surfactant*, basically detergent, was included to prevent the frac water and formation oil from mixing together and emulsifying. Finally, *acid*, as described above, was pumped at the beginning of a frac stage to clean up drilling and perforating debris, to ensure that the frac fluid could be pumped into the reservoir.

The frac recipe was soon pretty standardized, and the procedure became commonplace. This was the design used by Henry & Landenberger when they began drilling Spraberry wells in 1971. Today's fracs, which are basically what I have described above (although few use guar—more on the important development of "slickwater" fracs later), are about 95% water, 4% sand and 1% chemicals.

A Forgivable Step in the Wrong Direction

As hydraulic fracturing was gaining early popularity, a stranger from outside the petroleum industry arrived on the frac scene and conducted a set of surprising experiments.

In 1958, the US Atomic Energy Commission initiated *Project Plowshare*. Plowshare was a research and development program, created to explore the use of nuclear explosives for industrial applications, in the hope that the relatively inexpensive energy available from such explosions could prove broadly beneficial for peaceful endeavors. The project's name was derived from a passage in the Bible, in which the prophet Micah foretold that "they shall beat their swords into plowshares, and their spears into pruning hooks; nation shall not lift up sword against nation, neither shall they learn war anymore" (Micah 4:3b, quoted from the *English Standard Version*). Granting that the verse was taken out of its Christological context—don't let the government do your exegesis—nevertheless this was a very laudable enterprise. So far, so good.

The program considered several uses for nukes in its initial decade, and in 1967, an application was first attempted in the petroleum industry. Here things got a little dubious: as if gunpowder, nitro and napalm weren't exciting enough, the commission decided to deploy nukes for the stimulation of low permeability gas reservoirs.

The first test, named Gasbuggy, was conducted in rural New Mexico, east of Farmington, on December 10, 1967. A well was drilled to 4227 feet, and a 29-kiloton (kt) bomb was detonated in it. For comparison, the "Little Boy" bomb dropped on Hiroshima in 1945 had about half that yield. Setting aside for the moment that the resulting production rate was low, the larger problem was that the produced gas was contaminated with radioactivity. Apparently, this wasn't entirely expected…?

In yet another example of the *mo' is better* mantra, a larger explosion—this one 40 kt—was conducted on September 10, 1969, in Garfield County, Colorado. This test was called Rulison. The resulting production rate was again low, and of course the gas was still contaminated, although this time they had included some measures to reduce its radioactivity.

Refusing to give up, the program conducted a third experiment with a still larger explosion. The Rio Blanco test took place in the vicinity of Rifle, Colorado on May 17, 1973, and detonated a knee-knocking 99 kt (in three stages of 33 kt each). The results were reminiscent of the old carpenter's joke, "I've cut this board twice and it's still too short": the gas was still radioactive. But at least the production rate was low.

The program was thankfully terminated in 1977.

What Exactly Does a Frac Look Like?

Imagine a well that has been drilled and cased to a depth of, say, 9000 feet, then perforated in the pay zone near the bottom of the wellbore. The frac crew and all its pumps and equipment are assembled in place, revved up and ready to start the procedure. The pumps begin to push fluid down the hole at a rate exceeding the formation's ability to drink it, and the wellbore pressure starts to build. As the pressure builds, the pumps continue pumping, and something has to give.

The weak point in the frac plumbing system is not the massive pumps, not the fluid manifold and piping, not the casing cemented into the wellbore, all of which are designed to withstand very high pressures. The weak point is the formation itself. In response to the tremendous pressure being exerted upon it down the casing and through the perforations, the rock layer parts—it *fractures*.

So what does that look like down there? First, as Hubbert had rightly proved, the crack that forms in deeper reservoirs is *vertical.* From top to bottom the fracture curtain is about 200–300 feet. In the present illustration, with the pay zone at 9000 feet, the fracture is entirely contained more than a mile and a half below the earth's surface. That mile and a half of overburden absorbs practically all the energy released by the fracturing, so if you are standing on location you neither hear nor feel it.

As pressure continues to be applied by pumping fluid into the wellbore at a high rate (usually 90–100 barrels per minute these days), the fracture extends, or *propagates,* outward from the wellbore and farther into the formation. It extends on both sides, like the wings of the finial eagle atop a US flagpole; in fact, in oil field parlance, the fractures on either side of the wellbore are referred to as *frac wings.* When the frac stage is finished, the wings extend outward 300–600 feet on either side of the wellbore. The fracture then is not one-dimensional like a hairline crack, but a two-dimensional feature, like a curtain or a *plane,* about 300 feet tall and 1000 feet from one side to the other, with the wellbore near its center. I say *near* rather than *at* its center because frac wings are not necessarily symmetrical—often one side is longer than the other.

And to be accurate, the fracture is not a solitary plane, but more like a zone or *swarm* of multiple, crisscrossing cracks all aligned in a similar orientation. The width of each fracture is very narrow, no more than a few millimeters, and the surfaces are not smooth but rough and irregular. The sand that was pumped in the fluid is now dispersed throughout the fracture network, preventing the cracks from closing after the pumping stopped. The fracture network then provides a pathway, allowing hydrocarbons to flow continually through the formation and into the wellbore.

Fracking at the End of the 20ᵗʰ Century

During the remainder of the century, following the nuclear *faux pas*, there were a few incremental improvements in the fracking process. Service companies developed synthetic, high-strength proppants for use in ultra-deep, high-pressure/high-temperature reservoirs called *hostile environments*. They also produced a steady stream of secret-sauce fluid additives touted to improve results, but only a few yielded any meaningful gain. The heavy equipment used in fracking operations became more powerful and efficient, and pretty much everything was computerized. And as a result of the Exxon Valdez oil spill in 1989, fracking, along with every other cog in the petroleum machine, was made safer and less environmentally disruptive over time, as operators and vendors alike were pressured to clean up their collective act.

Through all these improvements in theory and practice, two components had remained axiomatic for frac success: thick fluid and a lot of proppant. But as the century drew to a close, some outside-the-box thinking and rogue experimentation were underway that would challenge the status quo and catapult fracking to the next level. In the Permian Basin, Henry Petroleum would be a prime mover in this leap.

Chapter 9
Another Dennis

A WORLD-CLASS OIL play, due to be dubbed "the Wolfberry," was about to happen. Henry would recognize potential that other operators had missed, and begin the play with a stealthy land grab ringing the entire basin. When reports of Henry's success leaked, scores of other operators would scramble into the play, mustering hundreds of rigs, leasing hundreds of thousands of acres, and eventually producing hundreds of millions of barrels of oil. Within a decade, the Wolfberry would raise the Permian Basin to the top of the global oil chart, as the vertical play turned sideways into the hot horizontal shale play of today.

The epic was made possible by the combination of two essential components: the right rocks and the right frac. The right rocks consisted in oil-rich shale source beds and porous limestone reservoir, occurring together in the right proportions. For several decades, researchers had speculated about the existence of such a geologic mixture in a ring around the floor of the basin's perimeter. No one had actually proven it, although a few operators, poking around

164

the ring, had chanced upon small oil accumulations that hinted at something more. But these drillers did not see the big-picture potential, and made no attempt to develop it. The right frac had also been known for several years, an unorthodox design called a *slickwater* frac (more on that technique later). But this frac was being used in other basins and for different reasons. Many Permian Basin operators had never heard of it, and none of them was using it.

Both critical components—the rocks and the frac—were providentially handed to Henry, along with a few people who had the smarts to synthesize the pieces and recognize the potential. Henry management also had the requisite moxie, and would make a huge financial gamble on the play before any conclusive proof had been found. The gamble would pay off, as Henry would go on to prove the existence of the play, then figure out how to make it commercially successful on a basin-sized scale.

The rock piece came to Henry in mid-2002, unexpectedly, when Gary Pitts was at another company's office pursuing a possible MIP deal. (We'll get to Gary's tale in the next few chapters.) But the frac piece arrived about a year and half earlier, inadvertently, in the mind of a consulting engineer. I introduced Dennis Phelps at the end of Chapter 7, when Van Temple needed help evaluating the McCamey MIP. Dennis at the time was in East Texas, retired, but with an unfinished financial matter that needed to be addressed.

Dennis's backstory is very important to the plot, so I'm going to back up several years and follow him as he works out the frac design that would come to unlock the Wolfberry.

———————————

Dennis Phelps began his petroleum career in 1970. After graduating with a mechanical engineering degree, he spent a decade working for ARCO, then worked for consulting firms for another ten years in Midland and Tyler, before rejoining ARCO in Midland in 1989.

A few years later, Tony Best—who would soon become Henry's partner at the Shafter Lake MIP—became president of ARCO Permian, and consequently Dennis's boss. Tony wanted to book a lot of reserves quickly and cheaply, and he tasked Dennis with finding them. ARCO owned a substantial acreage position in two giant old oilfields, Pegasus (familiar to the reader by now) and Wilshire. Many of the company's wells were not only old (1950s vintage) but they were also deep, with TDs in the Ellenburger Formation below 13,000 feet. Dennis identified Pegasus in particular as ripe for reserves harvest, and he went to work plugging back these wells from their original deep reservoirs to shallower pay zones, the same as Henry was doing at the Mobil MIP (a large oil field may have several different operators working in it at the same time).

Dennis's target of choice was the gas-productive Penn Sand at about 10,000 feet. The Penn at Pegasus is *tite* (low permeability), and he was stimulating it with a traditional frac design of thick fluid and high sand concentration. At one of his fracs in 1997, Dennis had a curious experience. The crew had just finished pumping the frac *pad*—a volume of sand-free fluid at the start to establish and widen a fracture in preparation for the sand-laden phase. Then, as they began pumping the sand, one of the pumps broke down and the frac *screened out*. A screen-out occurs when the sand entrained in the fluid begins to pile up at the perforations, instead of being carried out of the wellbore into the formation. When the pump broke, the pump-in pressure lessened, allowing the fracture to relax and narrow. The sand stacked out at the perforations, plugging up the wellbore, and the wellhead pressure spiked. The operation was immediately shut down.

All of this was fairly common; equipment routinely breaks down on frac jobs. Dennis decided not to try to re-frac the zone after the wellbore was cleaned out, even though he had been able to get only a little sand into the reservoir on the initial attempt. He had the crew place the well on production, and—here's the curious part—it started making as much gas as wells successfully fracked with a lot of sand.

This happened a few more times, even without equipment breakdowns: the crew would not be able to establish a fracture wide enough to admit sand, the frac would be shut down prematurely, and the well would end up producing at about the same rate as other wells completed with a full frac. Because these shut-down jobs had pumped so little sand and gel, the fracs cost much less than the traditional design. Dennis had inadvertently achieved the result he was seeking: reserves on the cheap.

"So much for doing it accidentally," Dennis thought, "why not do it on purpose?"

He determined to pump a frac sans sand. In planning the job, Dennis had told his frac consultant, "Here's my deal: I'm gonna pump a pad—a big, big pad. And then I'm gonna just taper in a little bit of sand, just to hold the perfs open." In other words, he would significantly increase the volume of sand-free fluid to make it the major part of the frac. He would follow that with a smaller volume of fluid containing only a little sand, just enough to prop the fracture near the wellbore, to ensure open communication between the wellbore and the formation through the perforations. "And sure enough, the well came in." The cheap, low-sand frac, pumped intentionally this time, was again as effective as the high-dollar, sand-packed model.

Dennis referred to his design as a "slickwater" frac—mostly water with some friction reducer, some bactericide, and a little bit of guar gel in the sand-laden phase to assist in carrying the sand.

His slickwater key had unlocked the Penn—would it open anything else?

On some of ARCO's acreage, Dennis had noted geologic similarities between the Penn and the basal Wolfcamp reservoir lying above it. Granted, the Wolfcamp was an oil-producing carbonate (specifically a *detrital limestone*) whereas the Penn was a gas-producing sandstone. But the reservoirs were mechanically similar: both were tite with high *fracture gradients* (requiring very high pressure to initiate a fracture). "So why don't we try the same thing in the Wolfcamp?" Dennis identified a Wolfcamp plugback candidate and fracked it with a lot of slickwater and only a little sand. The well came on flowing at more than 100 BOPD, five times the rate he normally achieved. OK, great—but was it a fluke or was it science? The job could have been a perfect-storm one-off, or in Dennis's words, a *hallelujah!* well. He tried again, and this next well came in at a startling 300 BOPD and stayed there for weeks before beginning to decline. So science it was, just as with the Penn.

To this point, the slickwater fracs had been a "cost-saving measure," Dennis said, clearly successful because the resulting Penn production was as good as it had been with the more expensive traditional frac. But here was something new: the slickwater results in the Wolfcamp were actually better than those from traditional design jobs in that formation, *much* better. He saw a twofer in the making: cheaper frac *and* more reserves, at least for some formations. Although he had theories about why the new design worked on these tite rocks, he could not say for sure. But not knowing the why wasn't going to keep him from making more great wells.

Might this technique work on other formations at other places? Dennis began to think outside the Pegasus box.

———

Tony and Dennis had not been relying solely on the plugback program to add reserves; they were also drilling new wells. To that end, Tony had recently acquired a sizeable acreage position in southern Midland County. He told Dennis that some Spraberry drillers had begun adding what they called "Wolfcamp tails" to their wells: that is, they did not TD the wells in the Spraberry, but kept going down through the Dean and a few hundred feet into the underlying Wolfcamp. This practice of completing a little Wolfcamp with the Spraberry was adding modest reserves, and that sounded like a plan to Dennis.

He contracted two small rigs, capable of drilling to about 10,000 feet, that were considerably less expensive than bigger, deep-drilling rigs. The top of the Wolfcamp under ARCO's acreage was at about 9300 feet, so these rigs could get him 700 feet of "tail" in the formation. Dennis then established a routine of drilling to 10,000 feet, and fracking two intervals in the Wolfcamp and two in the Spraberry using a traditional, thick-gel high-sand design. To this point, the program had yielded marginal results.

But, in the fall of 1998, as he was thinking about where to test his new slickwater design outside of the Pegasus workover program, Dennis considered the Wolfcamp tails in his drilling program: since the frac worked on the Wolfcamp at Pegasus, maybe it would work at the drilling acreage as well. One of his rigs had just drilled the sixth of an eight-well program on the company's MT Boulting-house 11 lease, off the western flank of Pegasus Field, in southern Midland County. This was much nearer the Central Basin Platform than his previous drilling, and Dennis had observed more detrital limestone in the Wolfcamp here, relative to locations farther to the east. He had also noticed that the initial producing rates at these Boultinghouse wells, even with traditional fracs, were twice that of the eastern wells. Not being a geologist, Dennis did not recognize a link between these observations, but he filed them in his mental cabinet and went on with his frac work.

Dennis revised his original completion plan for the seventh Boultinghouse well: he fracked the Wolfcamp in two separate intervals with his slickwater design, and left off the Spraberry altogether, in order to determine how much oil his Wolfcamp tails were capturing. Even without help from the Spraberry, for the ten months that Dennis tracked the well, the Boultinghouse #7 produced as much oil as wells that had been fracked with more stages and a traditional design. And the cost was much lower.

In addition to his new frac design, Dennis had made a few other important adjustments to the traditional Spraberry drilling paradigm. He had started pumping his fracs at a higher rate, 50 barrels per minute as opposed to the standard 25–30, and, though he was not sure why, production increased as a result. Accordingly, he began running 5½-inch casing—that is, the outside diameter of the pipe is five and a half inches—in place of the 4½-inch pipe traditionally used by Spraberry operators (larger pipe reduces friction, which allows for faster pump-in rates). Dennis also *clustered* all his perforations within a twenty-foot interval of the borehole, thereby focusing the pumping pressure, to create longer frac wings and open a greater area of the formation for production; traditionally, perforations were spread over a much longer interval in the borehole. He saw all these modifications—the slickwater design, larger pipe, higher treating rates and shorter perforation intervals—as a package deal: all of them were necessary for achieving the improved production.

In March 1999, BP America announced its intention to buy ARCO for $27 billion. The deal included the company's Permian Basin subsidiary, ARCO Permian, where Dennis had worked for the past ten years, and he accepted a voluntary severance package in August. He was 53, a thirty-year veteran of the oil industry, and had done well for himself. Now, he only wanted to golf and go fishing for a while. His and his wife's aging parents were all living in East Texas, so he and Judy decided to purchase a house on a private lake near Hawkins. He knew he could find work in that neck of the woods, if needed.

Dennis shared his frac modifications and results with ARCO colleagues who were staying on with BP. The team had plans to drill immediately south of the Boultinghouse, on the JT Lynch 14 lease, and Dennis wanted them to have every chance of success after he was gone.

He also tucked away this knowledge for himself. After all, you never know...

In fall 1999, Dennis Phelps was leaving Midland. He had made good friends and fishing buddies, among them Dennis Johnson and Gary Pitts. All three men and their wives attended the same Sunday school class at First Baptist. Before setting out, Dennis had a goodbye lunch with Dennis Johnson, and geological manager Dave Feavel tagged along. Knowing Henry's history with the Spraberry, Phelps told them a little about his Wolfcamp tails program at ARCO: "I've got a new Wolfcamp frac technique that I just, kind of, deducted, that I'd like to tell you about, if you ever need some Spraberry help." He also told Dave about the excellent results at the Boultinghouse lease, which could not be explained by his frac alone as he had only deployed it on one of the eight lease wells: "Look at the Boultinghouse; we saw something over there in the geology that was different, and the production is very good."

And then he was off. On a morning in early October 1999, Dennis Phelps turned his truck east onto I-20, fixed Midland in his rear-view mirror, and looked forward to the Piney Woods of East Texas.

But *the best-laid schemes o' mice an' men gang aft agley*. A year later, Dennis's Midland house was still on the market, and he decided to return to Midland and do consulting work until it sold. So, in the fall of 2000, he called Dennis Johnson to see if Henry had any projects on which he might assist. Henry did not currently have Spraberry drilling plans, Johnson told Phelps, but

Van Temple could use his help evaluating a potential waterflood project at McCamey.

So Phelps returned to Midland, a year after leaving, and set up temporary shop in Henry's office. He worked the evaluation with Van through March 2001, took a few months off, then returned in June for what was to be the McCamey wrap-up. Phelps saw high risk and low reward in the project: "I told them not to do it."

By this point, waterfloods had been fueling Henry's growth for a decade, and the successes at Phoenix, Shafter Lake and East Ackerly Dean had even won some local fame for the company. But now, the waterflood candidates were drying up, and at McCamey, one of the last opportunities the team was able to land, Phelps was recommending a pass without even trying. But unbeknownst to the team, and even to himself, he was also carrying one of the two essential components that would soon launch Henry to stardom on a completely different course.

Dennis's Midland house sold in the summer, and he went to Hawkins for good, or so he thought. Three months later came 9/11, and as a result, in Dennis's words, "My retirement fund was cut in half." At the same time, McCamey was refusing to die, so Dennis returned in October to earn more retirement cash and to help the flood along, in one direction or another. He then holidayed back at his lake home, and returned to Midland in February 2002, to administer McCamey's official last rites.

At the end of March, with his Midland house sold, McCamey buried, and his nest egg replenished, Dennis Phelps made ready to retry his retirement. A year and a half after his first farewell to Dennis Johnson, he said goodbye a second time, and again offered to help Henry with its Spraberry programs: "Oh by the way, remember—I got this new Wolfcamp frac technique." And he was off to his long overdue date with a boat and some bass. Surely nothing would deter him now...

Chapter 10
Setting the Wolfberry Stage

ONE OF THE two essential Wolfberry components was now in place. Well, it was in East Texas. But its link to Henry had been established. Dennis Phelps had developed a new frac design that worked wonderfully on the Wolfcamp tails in his drilling program. He had offered it, twice, to Dennis Johnson, who had promised to take him up on it if an opportunity arose. So the right frac, the engineering piece of the pair, was in place. Albeit incognito.

The other component, the right rocks, was headed Henry's way, but it would take a geologist's mind to perceive it. As with the frac, the right rocks came as a by-product of a different project.

Around the time that Dennis Phelps was fracking the Boulting-house #7 with his slickwater design, CMS Oil & Gas entered the Permian Basin. The company, a subsidiary of Michigan-based CMS Energy Corp, began drilling horizontal Devonian wells on a farmout from Texaco in west-central Midland County. They soon added a Spraberry program on the same acreage. CMS's development operations were overseen by one Danny Campbell, a degreed petroleum engineer and sometime banker who had worked at Chase Bank in Midland before striking out on his own as a consultant. He later joined CMS as a division manager in 2001.

When Danny came onboard and scoped the company's Spraberry program, he saw that it needed to produce about 10 MBOE for every $100,000 of investment in order to meet his economic hurdle rate. As his all-in cost was $600,000 per well, the wells had to make 60 MBOE each. These reserves were reasonable for a Spraberry well in the vicinity of CMS's acreage, and the team had a good chance of succeeding. But Danny wanted some cushion.

To juice the reserves and the program's economics, Danny's team came up with the idea of drilling deeper, through the Dean and into the Wolfcamp, in hopes of penetrating some additional pay zones. This was the original Wolfcamp tails program that Tony Best and Dennis Phelps were copying on ARCO's acreage. At first, CMS's tails were about 500 feet, which accommodated one or two frac stages and increased production slightly. But occasionally, they lucked into what Danny called a "blip" in the Wolfcamp. *Blip* is a not-too-technical term for the occasional high-porosity, oil-productive detrital limestone bed sometimes encountered in the Wolfcamp out in the deep part of the basin. Such blips—also referred to with equal imprecision as *pimples* and *pods*—yielded a quick surge of oil, but they were usually small (hence the nicknames) and soon depleted. However short-lived, the extra oil quickly produced did wonders for CMS's Spraberry economics.

A few of CMS's blip wells, though, had staying power. Once stimulated, these zones would flow for a few weeks without the aid of a pumping unit. That it was the Wolfcamp blips, and not the routine Spraberry zones, that were responsible for the flowing phenomenon was clear to the team by the color of the oil:

not traditional Spraberry green, but honey-colored, typical of the Wolfcamp.

Danny wanted to keep the flowing Wolfcamp blips secret from the offset operators, to give him a chance to grab additional acreage without competition. "I had made a deal for pumping units for all those wells, and my guys said, 'Well, the flowing ones don't need pumping units.' And I said, 'Put 'em on anyway. I don't want anybody to know these wells are flowing.'"

Certain that they were into something good, the CMS geologists started prospecting for more blips. Knowing that some of the coarser sand in the Spraberry period had entered the basin from the north, by way of underwater channels, Danny's team reasoned that the blip-forming Wolfcamp detritus might have come into the basin along the same trend. They set about using *well logs* to map the subsurface geology along a north-south vector between their two acreage blocks. (A well log is a record of electrical and chemical measurements, gathered by tools lowered into a borehole, that describes the characteristics of the various strata penetrated by the borehole.) Few wells had been drilled in the area, however, and consequently there were few logs for the team to use in their hunt.

But on they mapped, encouraged by the production they had already found. They identified more Texaco-owned acreage along that trend, and Danny was able to negotiate another farmout. The team then drilled their Spraberry wells with Wolfcamp tails, now penetrating 1000 feet into the formation in search of more blips, pimples and pods—which, before long, would point a Henry geoguy to Wolfberry treasure.

In the spring of 2002, Danny Campbell learned that the CMS parent in Michigan was going to divest its Permian Basin child. He saw potential in the company's vast acreage position, which extended beyond Midland into other West Texas counties and New

Mexico. Being a deal junkie after the order of Gary Pitts, Danny left the company before the sale closing and joined Community National Bank in Midland, aiming to raise money himself and bid competitively for CMS's assets.

Before embarking on his plan, he contacted Gary Pitts at Henry. Danny couldn't disclose the sale, but he did describe the potential of CMS's holdings. CMS had neither the manpower nor the capital to work these properties, he told Gary—maybe Henry could design a MIP-type deal to drill and hold the acreage? Henry had established a reputation for these kinds of arrangements, which is why Danny approached Gary. Also, Danny knew he'd have a good chance to join with Henry in developing the acreage if Henry was already operating the properties when CMS was sold: "I figured I'd be more likely to get a deal with Henry than with some unknown buyer in Timbuktu." (Danny would later join Henry and play a critical role in the company's continuing success.)

Gary duly opened talks with CMS in Midland, and by early May he was well on his way in the negotiation. But behind the scenes, the Michigan parent company had already reached terms with a buyer—not in Timbuktu, but in France: Perenco SA, an Anglo-French company with oil and gas operations around the world.

Even before the deal was made public, Perenco froze CMS's capital spending, thus requiring the company to cease all development activity. Gary saw this as an opening. He met the CMS manager for lunch and offered Henry's financial help with any drilling obligations that CMS needed to service. The manager told him about the Spraberry program on the Texaco farmout, where CMS was earning 320 acres for every well it drilled. But Texaco's continuous development terms were rigid: CMS needed to keep two rigs running there, and they were only allowed ten days between finishing one well and starting the next. If CMS did not stay on this treadmill, it would forfeit the remaining acreage, and at this time there were fourteen more wells to be drilled. With his capital frozen, the manager had to stop drilling. Gary told him, "We can handle that!" They hammered out a tentative agreement right there at the lunch table: Henry would slip into CMS's operator shoes and drill the remaining fourteen wells on the Texaco acreage. In return, Henry would keep 100% ownership of the wells they drilled and earn half of the acreage, and CMS would retain the other half so they could later drill their own wells. Henry would not pay any acreage cost, and there would be no back-ins or overrides for CMS.

Before the deal could be officially signed, Henry needed to do some quick due diligence. Geology manager Dave Feavel would normally have vetted CMS's geological files in this sort of venture, but he was on an extended vacation. So Gary scrubbed in for him (recall that Gary is a geophysicist by academic training).

At CMS's office, one of the company's geologists walked Gary through their Wolfcamp tails routine. The Wolfcamp in CMS's well logs was not much to look at, mostly silts and shales. On a few well logs, the geologist pointed out examples of the high-porosity detrital limestone beds—the blips—and explained that wells with these beds often flowed after being fracked. He told Gary that the team was prospecting for more of the limestones along a trend north and south of their acreage.

Suddenly, recognition flashed in Gary's mind. "Not a full-blown revelation," he recalled, "but a significant *aha!*" as his twenty-five years of prospecting in the Permian, reading technical articles and looking at well logs clicked into a coherent picture. He knew what those porous limestones actually were and he knew where to find more of them, much larger and thicker—and it wasn't to the north and south. If this scrappy Wolfcamp juiced CMS's production a little, the rocks that Gary was thinking of would juice it a lot.

Gary drove straight back to the office and grabbed a geological atlas from his bookshelf, something by University of Texas scholar William Galloway. He xeroxed one of Galloway's maps, and drew on it the entire play, as he anticipated it, "a band all the way around the Midland Basin." He took his map to Dennis Johnson, summarized the opportunity, and delivered his punch line: "This Wolfcamp tails play is going to work, but it's going to work much better in a different place. I've seen this detrital Wolfcamp with higher quality, and I know where to find it. This is the next big play—we can either be first, or we can be left behind!"

"Dennis Johnson is an enigma," as one of his comrades described him, because he is gifted with two skill sets seldom seated in the same soul: he can be logical, but also imaginative. He is like Jim in this way. Dennis listened to Gary, looked at the maps, and saw the future. "Well," he responded, "let's get Dave [Feavel] involved."

The second critical component of the Wolfberry play—the right rocks—had arrived at Henry. The first—the right frac—was still in East Texas, in a boat on a lake. And no one at Henry had yet recognized its importance, nor the power of combining the two.

Two threads were now developing simultaneously. Gary and Dave would soon be laser-focused on a mapping mission to identify the precise location of the "better Wolfcamp" that Gary had seen in his epiphany. And Dennis Phelps was about to be summoned, along with his slickwater frac, to assist with the CMS project. Within a few months, the two parallel threads would converge. The Wolfberry was about to lift off.

———————

Henry and CMS signed their agreement in mid-June, and the Henry team assembled a presentation and commenced shopping for a partner. Pioneer was their third showing and took 70% of the project while Henry kept the rest. Mike LaMonica commandeered two rigs and spudded the first well, the Emily #1, on July 9, three weeks ahead of schedule and less than a month after the signing. Oil was now at $27, up from $20 at the beginning of the year. Henry had picked up fourteen drilling locations for free and, for the first time, would be adding trendy Wolfcamp tails to its traditional Spraberry paradigm. Everything was looking good.

As the Emily # 1 was spudding, Dennis Johnson recalled the conversation with his Sunday school friend, Dennis Phelps—something about a new frac design Phelps had used on ARCO's Wolfcamp tails with excellent results. Phelps had offered to introduce the design to Henry if an opportunity ever arose.

Now, one had arose. So Dennis Johnson called Dennis Phelps. Phelps remembered that exchange, word for word:

"We've got a farmout in the Pegasus area. Isn't that where you were doing that work with your new frac?"

"Yes, it's real close."

"I want to drill fourteen wells this summer. Do you want to do your Wolfcamp frac?"

"Sure."

"Well, c'mon back."

Phelps stowed his fishing gear and returned to Midland in early July. Shortly after his arrival, Henry management convened to hear him present his rendition of the Wolfcamp tails routine, which Henry intended to copy. They particularly wanted to hear about his newfangled frac technique. When he was done, Mike LaMonica said what the others were thinking: "Dennis, you're crazy."

Dennis wasn't crazy. And his frac wasn't newfangled.

Elsewhere in the country, a handful of folks had been using low-sand, thin-fluid designs for the past 30 years. In the 1970s, operators in the Hugoton Field in western Kansas and Oklahoma routinely threw suction lines into the Cimarron River and pumped water and sand directly into their wellbores. They called the procedure a "river frac." In the 80s, Union Pacific Resources Company (UPRC) experimented in the Austin Chalk with what they called "water fracs," water containing no proppant and no guar gel at all, only a bit of acid. The fracs were successful, and they tried a similar design on the Niobrara Formation at their acreage in Wyoming, this time to no avail. In the mid-90s, UPRC deployed a modified version of the frac, with very little sand in a fluid composed of water and friction reducer, at their East Texas Basin properties producing gas from the Cotton Valley sandstone. Their initial goal was simply to cut costs, but they soon discovered that many of the treated wells produced better than those fracked with a conventional design. The company later shared their new design with other East Texas operators, who experienced similar success.

UPRC's experiments and results parallel those of Dennis Phelps, who was working on his own design in the Permian Basin just a few months behind them. Although UPRC published a few papers on their work in the late 90s, knowledge of the slickwater frac had not made it to West Texas at any practical level, perhaps because of the remoteness, perhaps because UPRC's work was in a gas reservoir, and the Permian is mostly an oil province. Whatever the reasons, Dennis was not aware that a frac design like the one that he had recently "deducted" was already being used in other places. He had not read their papers, which were published around the time he was first applying his slickwater design to the Wolfcamp. At ARCO, he was busy feeding the rig monster and completing wells and had little time for reading. As he put it, "ARCO didn't pay me to do literature searches."

There is no question that UPRC and BJ Services (the frac vendor working with UPRC) deserve credit for pioneering the slickwater frac technique on an industry scale. And there is no question that Dennis Phelps merits the same credit on the local scale of the Permian Basin.

After scrambling to spud the Emily #1 in July, Henry drilled all fourteen wells required to gain the remaining acreage, completing the last one in January 2003. All the wells were drilled to 10,500 feet, giving them 1200 feet of Wolfcamp tail. And Dennis Phelps, notwithstanding his initial reception, had been allowed to deploy his complete repertoire: 5½" casing, twenty-foot perforation clusters, and of course a slickwater frac on the Wolfcamp, along with a traditional design on the Spraberry.

The initial producing rates of Henry's wells were very similar to those achieved previously by CMS in their wells. Their early declines were also similar. So the frac did work: it was equally effective as the traditional design, even though in this case it had not increased production. But Phelps had cautioned the Henry team from the start: "This isn't a panacea. It's not going to improve every reservoir."

The team was not completely convinced yet, but they were intrigued. They wanted to try the frac in other situations, to see if they could find some rock for which the frac would actually increase production, as it had for Dennis in the Wolfcamp at Pegasus.

It turns out that Gary Pitts had already found some.

Chapter 11
Birth of the Wolfberry

GARY'S *AHA!* AT CMS's office was not revelation but recognition—a realization of something already in existence. Or at least, thought to exist.

For a few decades, geologists researching the Permian Basin had described a potential oil play that they called "Wolfcampian basinal carbonates." As discussed in the Rocks for Jocks chapter, during Wolfcamp time, carbonate sediments accumulating on the shallow platform and around the basin rim were occasionally dislodged and tumbled down the slope into deep water where shales were being deposited. The detritus piled up in heaps at the bottom, or spread out in underwater deltas extending a few miles across the basin floor. This circumstance put porous limestone reservoir rock and oil-sourcing shales together in the same place.

At the time Gary was in CMS's office, the play was more of a speculation than a proven fact. A few operators had found production within the area, but the discoveries were generally small and relatively isolated. A notable exception is the Amacker Tippett

Field in central Upton County, which was the strongest evidence of the play to that time. Amacker Tippett is situated on the basin floor, at the bottom of the shelf slope. The first Wolfcamp producer there was completed in 1955, a chance encounter by a driller who was looking for something deeper. In the late 70s and early 80s, drillers developing deep reservoirs at the field frequently penetrated productive zones in the Wolfcamp on the way down. Geologists rightly interpreted these as massive blocks of shallow-water deposits that had slumped down onto the basin floor. Operators then began using seismic to locate more blocks, and by the end of the 80s, the field had made 16 million barrels of Wolfcamp oil and still had more on tap.

Gary himself had drilled wells at Amacker Tippett in the 80s. He was well acquainted with the play concept through research journals and industry conferences, and these experiences and studies coalesced for his *aha!* He saw that CMS had the right idea of adding Wolfcamp tails, and they might make some good wells. But they would not make great wells, because they were searching in the wrong area. The play model indicated that the best Wolfcamp detrital deposits were not along a north-south trend in the deep basin, as CMS suspected, but around the basin's perimeter.

Looking back, Gary likens his epiphany to a scene in *Raiders of the Lost Ark*. Indiana Jones and his friend, Sallah, have asked an aged imam to decipher ancient script on the headpiece of the Staff of Ra. The staff will locate the Well of Souls, where the Ark of the Covenant is buried. A cadre of Nazis have done their own deciphering, built a replica staff, identified the location, and are already busy excavating. But when the imam translates the instructions on the reverse side of Indy's headpiece—the side the Nazis lack—Indy and Sallah realize that the Nazis' locator staff is too long, and they exclaim in unison, "They're digging in the wrong place!"

When Dave returned from vacation, Gary told him about the CMS wells and his idea about making the detrital play. Like Gary, Dave Feavel was a twenty-five-year geo-veteran of the Permian Basin. He, too, had read journals, attended conventions, looked at logs and mapped prospects. And he also had personal experience in the Amacker Tippett Field, having drilled there with another company in the 1980s. He knew the play, and had created his own name for it: "the garbage dump," an apt description of the base of the slope where the shelf-shed detritus piled up.

Using logs from the handful of wells that had been drilled west of the CMS acreage nearer the carbonate shelf, Dave began mapping where he and Gary believed the play would be found. And when Dennis Phelps returned to assist with the CMS project, Dave caught up with him on ARCO's excellent production at the Boultinghouse lease, where Phelps had deployed his new frac on a Wolfcamp well. Back then, Phelps had told Dave that the quality of the rocks must be primarily responsible for the excellent results, but he also believed that his frac made a difference. At that time, in August 1999, ARCO had not yet released their well logs to public domain—the RRC allows operators to hold back certain technical data for a period of time—so Dave was unable to evaluate the geology of the lease. But he was able to access the lease production data, which cannot be held confidential. The Boultinghouse wells had been producing for about a year, and though they had started out strong, the early decline was steep. Dave was not impressed: "They were dropping like a rock, straight down, headed for an ultimate production of about 50 MBO. I thought, "It doesn't look like they're going to hold up." He had written them off.

Now, two years later, with the Wolfcamp detrital play on his mind as he and Phelps debriefed, Dave realized that the Boultinghouse lease was near the shelf margin, and therefore likely positioned within the play that he and Gary were exploring. He swung back around for another look.

The well logs had still not been released, but Dave revisited the production data. The lease had now been producing for three years, and behold: the decline, so steep at Dave's first assessment, had "broken over" abruptly after twenty months and was now much gentler. In fact, the wells had already produced about 40 MBO each, fully twice as much as other Wolfcamp tails wells over the same amount of time. And they were on pace to make 100 MBO during their lifetime—much higher than average.

There had been other developments in the Boultinghouse neighborhood during the interim. Before being acquired by BP, ARCO had secured the JT Lynch 14 lease, immediately south of the Boultinghouse. BP had later completed all eight wells on the lease, using Dennis's twenty-foot perforation clusters and slickwater design in the Wolfcamp stages. But they had run 4½-inch pipe, rather than his preferred 5½, which had surely limited the frac pumping rate, and consequently the wells were not fully-fledged Phelps. But in the two years since they were drilled, the Lynch wells had produced nearly as much as the Boultinghouse and were now on the same gentler decline.

The Boultinghouse-Lynch specialness had attracted other operators. Ex-ARCO employees who abandoned BP had dispersed to other companies, taking their knowledge about Phelps's design with them. Two Midland operators got inside scoops from the exes, and attempted to duplicate the results themselves. Both operators enlisted the not-too-technical technique of "close-ology": they identified where good production had already been established, and then drilled close to it. Operators often use close-ology, sometimes successfully, although the reasoning is not necessarily sound given the geologic variability of some formations.

In addition to the two local operators, BP itself had attempted to extend the good production. The company stepped a few miles west and leased several sections from Texaco in the Sweetie Peck Field. Sweetie Peck was discovered in the 1950s and had been developed mainly for deep Ellenburger and Devonian pay. BP acquired the acreage for the deep potential, but they were also interested in the shallower Spraberry and Wolfcamp. In late 2001, the company drilled five wells in section 33 of the Texaco farmout, all of which penetrated most of the Wolfcamp interval.

Dave examined the information available on the new wells drilled by BP and the two local operators. None of the well logs had been released, and he was not able to complete much meaningful mapping, but he scrutinized the production data. The two local operators were producing a little less than Boultinghouse-Lynch, but clearly better than CMS's Wolfcamp tails wells to the east. This was consistent with Dave's theory: wells closer to the shelf slope should have more detrital carbonate and, consequently, should make more oil.

BP's data, on the other hand, presented a conundrum. According to the play concept, BP had drilled in an even better location than the Boultinghouse lease—a few miles to the west, closer to the platform margin edge, closer to the garbage dump. But the initial production from these wells was unimpressive, the rates declined quickly, and the wells were now on a trend to make only about a quarter as much as the Boultinghouse-Lynch wells. The conundrum was exacerbated by the Henry team's assumption that BP completed the wells using Phelps's design, as they had at the Lynch lease—the design should have yielded production at least as good, perhaps even better. These data draped a pall on the team's play hopes. Were Dave and the team missing something?

Without access to BP's geological and engineering files, Dave and company couldn't do much to investigate. And Henry had plenty of very real oil wells and lease obligations that needed tending. So, in late fall of 2002, Dave set aside the slope-and-basin play dream and turned his attention to reality chores.

The last of the fourteen CMS wells was completed in January 2003. The rigs that Henry had contracted for the program were redirected to drill a few wells at different Henry properties, and would then be released to other companies. But Dennis Johnson didn't want to let them go. Oil had been hovering in the $25–30 per-barrel range for the past several months, but in February it spiked to $36, and there was hope of a sustained climb. Dennis wanted to capture the price premium before drilling costs increased to match it. He also wanted to test Gary and Dave's idea about the detrital Wolfcamp play.

"Is there a place we can do this?" he asked them.

Dave dusted off the map he had been working on prior to laying the idea aside. He told Dennis about BP's Sweetie Peck acreage west of Boultinghouse, and pointed out that BP had not drilled anything since 2001. They might be open to doing a deal. On the other hand, those wells had not been very productive, which was likely *why* BP had stopped drilling. As Dave was unable to assess the geological reasons for the failure, there would be significant risk to Henry if they acquired the acreage.

But Dave, Gary and Dennis agreed that the great potential of the play merited testing, and they proposed a farmout to BP, with one qualification: Henry would first need to see all the geological and engineering files for both Sweetie Peck and Boultinghouse. BP agreed, and in early March, Dave Feavel and Dennis Phelps, the rock guy and the frac guy, headed to BP to evaluate their respective components of the data.

The threads were about to converge.

Dave was finally able to look behind the Boultinghouse curtain. He recalls the moment he unfolded the first log and saw the Wolfcamp interval: "I said to Phelps, 'I know what this is!'" The rocks were exactly what Dave and Gary expected: thick intervals of detrital limestone, which explained the excellent production. "And I knew they weren't unique—they were part of a trend 150 miles long and ten miles wide." He had found his garbage dump.

Dave was elated, but only half done, and he now turned to the five poor producers that BP had drilled. Here, the conundrum worsened. The Wolfcamp section in these wells looked very similar to the Boultinghouse logs. "But why is the production so bad? I'm looking at the Boultinghouse logs beside these logs, and I'm not understanding what makes this better than that. The two leases are in the same part of the play, they're both in my garbage dump. They should have made good wells."

Meanwhile, Phelps was busy working his way through the drilling records and completions files of the poor producers. Within a few hours, he began to see some devil in the details. The files showed that the Sweetie Peck wells were neither drilled nor fracked with his designs. Dennis scored each well on a matrix he devised on the spot, assigning relative values to the chief components of his Wolfcamp drilling and completion panoply: 5½-inch pipe, high treating rate, twenty-foot perforation clusters, low-viscosity fluid and low-sand concentrations. The BP wells scored miserably: small pipe, low treating rates, inconsistent perforating styles and a variety of frac recipes. One well had no Wolfcamp completion at all, and two others were not fracked but only acidized. He concluded that the wells on average were about 70% deficient.

Phelps relayed his findings to Dave: "I told him they weren't getting the Wolfcamp contribution. I said, 'These aren't my fracs.' And Dave said, 'Hallelujah!'"

As it turned out, the ARCO folks who had known Phelps and his method were still at BP in 2000 when the Lynch wells were drilled, and they had mostly stuck to his scheme. But those folks left BP before the Sweetie Peck wells were drilled a year later. The new team didn't know Phelps and had never heard about his design. And they clearly were unaware that the Wolfcamp, not the Spraberry, was the critical contributor in the tails wells. The conundrum was resolved: the problem wasn't the rock—it was the completion.

At this moment, Dave had his own epiphany: "I describe it as like Indiana Jones in the Well of Souls, when the beam of light suddenly shoots through the crystal and illuminates the location of the Ark of the Covenant." (You are not experiencing *déjà vu*: this is the *second* account in which a Henry geo-scientist, in the spring of 2003, looking at files in another company's office, has something like a revelation of the Wolfcamp detrital play, which he likens to a scene in *Indiana Jones: Raiders of the Lost Ark*.)

———————

Dave and Phelps returned from BP's office and reported their discoveries to Gary and Dennis Johnson. They all agreed that the play warranted pursuing, so Henry should take the BP farmout. Jim approved the move, with his usual qualification that they find a partner, and the farmout was signed a few weeks later on March 20. As in the CMS agreement, Gary had negotiated a deal in which Henry would not be charged an acreage fee: Henry would do the favor of keeping BP's acreage intact by drilling the wells required by Texaco, and BP in turn would give Henry 100% of every location drilled, from the surface to the top of the Penn Formation (meaning that Henry would own the rights to the entire Wolfcamp interval).

With the leases secured, Gary Pitts, Bill Fair and Van Temple built a presentation and started shopping for a partner in the Sweetie Peck Prospect, as they had dubbed it. On April 12, three weeks after receiving the farmout, the team signed an agreement with Entre Energy Partners, in which Henry would keep a 33% working interest and receive from Entre an acreage payment. One month later, on May 14, Henry spudded the Caitlin #2801, named for Pitts's eldest granddaughter.

The Wolfberry play had begun.

[*Author's note: I will here begin using the play nickname, "Wolfberry," to avoid being wordy, but the Henry team did not actually coin that term until a few years later.*]

_____

With the Caitlin drilling ahead, Dave resumed his mapping effort. He and Gary knew the approximate location of the right rocks—the band of detrital carbonates at the bottom of the slope. But there had not been enough drilling—that is, there were not enough well logs—to locate the band precisely, and he needed precision in order to determine which leases to pursue. Dave knew that the Amacker Tippett field was in the play trend, and now, having seen BP's logs, he knew that the Sweetie Peck and Boultinghouse leases, some twenty-five miles northwest, were in it as well. He focused his initial mapping on the area between them, relying primarily on the sparse well logs and patchy production in the area.

Dave needed some criterion by which to identify the play's *fairway*, the part that would have the greatest potential for success. Recall that the play requires the presence of two rock types—shale source rock and carbonate reservoir—mixed at optimal proportions. The edge of the band against the Central Basin Platform would have too much detrital carbonate and not enough shale, and the edge on the basin side would have the reverse problem. Dave figured those areas containing between 30% and 60% carbonate should perform the best, and he was using the logs to calculate percentages within the band.

While Dave was mapping and the Caitlin was drilling, the team learned that EOG Resources had a large acreage block right in the Amacker Tippett area, that they would likely be open to selling. Jim and Dennis wanted to continue acquiring acreage in the play, even before Henry had the Caitlin's results, to be ahead of the competition in case the well was successful. In response to Dennis's eager "where to next?" Dave and Gary pointed to the

EOG block. Dennis was for it, and Jim approved. Gary Pitts and landman Gary Elander worked out the deal with EOG in short order. Although they negotiated well, Pitts's free-acreage streak came to an end: Henry wrote a nominal check for the 3000 acres in exchange for a term assignment.

The EOG acquisition was proof that Henry was committed to the new play. On the day they signed the agreement, the Caitlin #2801 was drilling in the Grayburg Formation, still 4000 feet above the Wolfcamp. The well had not even reached its Wolfcamp target at Sweetie Peck, and yet Henry was paying for acreage and committing to drill wells twenty miles away, in the hope of a trend they believed in but had not proven.

As a result of this decision and its aftermath, the company would never again be thought of as just a little ol' Spraberry driller. Henry would soon be a player.

———————

Having committed to the play, securing more acreage was Henry's priority one. Guided by Dave's work-in-progress map of the fairway, Bill Fair and his team began a land-grab on scale unprecedented in Henry's history. Along with Gary Pitts, Dave Feavel and Dennis Johnson, Bill was a visionary in the Wolfberry win. A humble one: "I don't see my role in any of this [Wolfberry effort and success] as visionary. I see Dave and Gary as the visionaries, and Dennis, who was the one with the power to say, 'Yes, this is what we're going to do.' And then I just did my part."

The team intended to move the drilling rig to the EOG block as soon as the Caitlin was down, to quickly gain more information about the play. As in all of Henry's projects, they needed a partner for this second block. They offered it first to Entre, their partner at Sweetie Peck, but were told, "No, thank you, we have enough." So the search was on.

One evening, shortly after signing the EOG deal, Gary Pitts

was in the plumbing department at Home Depot, picking out potty parts for a do-it-yourself at home, when he saw his friend Newt Newton. Newt had been in upper management at ARCO during the years that Henry partnered with them at the Shafter Lake MIP. He had left ARCO at the BP buyout, and when Gary met him that night, he was working for Pure Resources.

Pure Resources was formed in 1999 by the merging of Midland-based Titan Exploration with Unocal's oil and gas operations in the Permian and San Juan Basins. Pure had promptly established a large acreage footprint in Upton County, near the Amacker Tippett field, and began drilling horizontal Devonian wells. In 2002, Unocal bought out the balance of Pure, emptied the C-Suite and hired Henry's friend Tony Best, who had also left ARCO, as president and CEO. Tony then invited Newt, his old sidekick, to rejoin him at Pure as the business development manager.

That evening at Home Depot, Gary suggested that Henry and Pure find a project to partner on, and he told Newt about Henry's new block near Amacker Tippett. Newt told Gary about Pure's acreage in the same area, and they set up a meeting. A few days later, Tony and Newt came to Henry's office to hear the Chickadee Prospect pitch. "Chickadee" was Henry's tongue-in-cheek code name for the project: as the team was aggressively searching for new Wolfcamp fields—read "WC fields"—they named it after the 1940 W. C. Fields flick, *My Little Chickadee*.

Tony and Newt needed little explanation of the play. At ARCO, they had watched Dennis Phelps develop and deploy his slickwater fracs, and they also knew the quality of the Boultinghouse rock. And after leaving ARCO, Newt had drilled offsets to the Boultinghouse lease with one of the local operators. But Tony and Newt had assumed the Boultinghouse to be a one-off, not realizing that it could be part of a potentially regional play. When Dave showed them a string of correlated well logs, demonstrating the continuity of the detrital Wolfcamp limestones from Boultinghouse and

Sweetie Peck all the way to Chickadee, they saw the light. "They were actually a little angry that we had already done Sweetie Peck without them," Dave said. "So it was an easy sell, quite frankly."

The group began spit-balling. The two companies had about 10,000 acres between them, at a roughly 25% Henry, 75% Pure split. They discussed pooling their acreage with those ownership proportions. Henry would be the operator, and any additional acreage acquired by either company in the area would be paid for and apportioned at the same split.

But Tony saw what Henry had seen: a play with basin-sized potential. He also saw how fast Henry made decisions and picked up acreage. He was fine with plans for the Chickadee *part*, but he wanted to be in on the *whole*: "Well then," he said, "I want to do a bigger deal."

Dave returned to his drafting table. He created a presentation covering the entire area that he had mapped to this point, which extended from the southern border of Sweetie Peck, down to the town of Rankin, and east to the Amacker Tippett area. He and Gary drew a polygon—which Gary dubbed "the Big Line"—enclosing the whole area: approximately twenty-five miles north-south and nineteen east-west, about 300,000 acres, which they planned to propose as the *area of mutual agreement* (AMI) for the Henry-Pure partnership.

But how much interest did Henry want to keep? Gary, Dave and a few other Henry managers wanted to retain more than Henry's usual 25%—this was the once-in-a-lifetime opportunity that every oilman dreams of, and they lobbied for 50%. On the other hand, once development got going, the capital investments would be substantial, even at 25%, and Henry would have to take on debt to keep up. If oil prices cratered and they couldn't pay their debt, what then? Not to mention that Henry had not completed a single well in the play—the Caitlin still had not yet even penetrated the Wolfcamp. In the end, Jim held the line: "We didn't have enough money to buy it all, and I didn't want to go in debt. So we stayed at a quarter." Jim closed the discussion with one of his Jim-isms: "Don't fall in love with your own stuff." Anyway, if the play were as big as anticipated, a quarter would be plenty.

The team reconvened with Pure, and again the sell was easy. The Wolfcamp Joint Venture (WCJV) was created on June 1. On that day, the Caitlin #2801 was drilling at 8650 feet, still a few hundred feet above the Wolfcamp. In less than three months, Henry had leased more than 15,000 acres in the play trend, secured 190 drillable locations, and created an AMI covering a third of Upton County—and they had not even caught a glimpse of the Wolfcamp in the first well.

––––––––––

Two weeks later, Henry spudded the initial Chickadee well. The Beverly #1, eighteen miles southeast of the Caitlin, was named for the Henrys' younger daughter. Meanwhile, the Caitlin TD'd on June 22 at 10,240 feet. The crew ran 5½-inch casing as Phelps had directed. The well was drilled through the entire Wolfcamp interval, as Dave and Gary believed there would as likely be reservoir at its base as near its top. So Henry had inverted the play: instead of drilling Spraberry wells with a Wolfcamp tail tacked on, Henry was drilling Wolfcamp wells with an uphole Spraberry option.

The Caitlin well logs were promising, with a Wolfcamp section about 1000 feet thick and numerous detrital limestone beds scattered in the shale—both of the requisite rock types were present. There was perhaps not as much clean limestone as Dave would have liked, but the well had clearly found the fairway. A frac crew moved in on July 2, superintended by Dennis Phelps himself, and began the planned completion: four slickwater fracs in the Wolfcamp and two traditionals in the Spraberry. The job finished, symbolically enough, on July 4.

On that same day at Chickadee, the Beverly reached total depth. The Wolfcamp here was thicker than at Sweetie Peck—some 1400 feet—and also had significantly more clean detrital limestone.

As the operations team was preparing the Beverly for completion, the crew at Sweetie Peck opened the wellhead valve on the Caitlin, and it began flowing oil on the first day—a promising sign. Several days later, when the flowing pressure had sufficiently dropped, the crew cleaned out the well, installed pumping equipment and placed it on production. For the first four days, the rate hovered in the 20–50 BOPD range. But on the fifth day it jumped to 188, then settled back to 120 for the next three weeks. This was a very good well.

A few weeks earlier, down south at Chickadee, a frac crew had rigged up on the Beverly. Again, Phelps was on location to superintend the work. After the frac and a bit of a rodeo during the cleanout—more on that later—the Beverly was opened up. It flowed over 100 BOPD for three weeks, a few days topping 140. As soon as the pressure dropped, the crew installed pumping equipment and placed the well on production. It went right back up to 140.

Another winner. Henry was two for two.

The Wolfberry was born.

Chapter 12
Growth Ballistic

HENRY HAD PROVEN the existence of a productive trend extending for at least twenty miles between Sweetie Peck and Chickadee. Dave and Gary were not surprised by the results—this was what they had anticipated from the combination of the right rocks and the right frac. The skeptics on the team, among them Van Temple and Mike LaMonica, were now converted. Even Dennis Phelps admitted that to this point he had been on the bubble, but now he also was convinced of the play potential.

Of course, the team had not proven the whole ring-around-the-basin play. Still, for the moment, Dennis Johnson was vindicated in his measured risk-taking, and Jim was beside himself with joy. "We were very euphoric…We had been looking for something like this for our entire career, and we had finally found it!" He attempted to calculate how much oil his team had proven producible from the trend between the two wells. The number was in the tens of millions of barrels.

Could that be right? He called Scott Tinker, director of the

Bureau of Economic Geology at the University of Texas, to double-check. Jim enjoined him to secrecy and filled him in. Scott agreed that Jim's ciphering was in order and that the accumulation was huge: "That would be the biggest oil find in Texas in the last fifty years."

The Henry-Pure partnership was on a Wolfberry mission even before the Caitlin and Beverly wells were completed. But now, with the proof of the two strong initial producing rates and the likelihood that the play extended well beyond Sweetie Peck and Chickadee, the partnership launched. For the next five years, Henry would conduct a dizzying campaign of land acquisition, drilling and production, ultimately growing the company to ten times its previous size.

The partnership's launch was fueled by three propellants. First was the partners' determination to tie up acreage ahead of the competition. While Henry was alone on the playing field for the moment, the partners knew that other operators would eventually catch on, and they wanted to get all the good pieces before that happened. Next was the growing list of drilling obligations resulting from the land grab. Each new lease required Henry to continue drilling wells on a set schedule, and if the team stumbled and missed a deadline, they could forfeit a great deal of acreage. Finally, there was a strong tailwind of rising oil prices. Oil was about $30 per barrel when Henry completed the Caitlin in mid-2003, and it had begun a steady climb that would take it to over $70 by summer of 2006.

Make hay while the sun shines.

Henry initially ran two drilling rigs in the play, and at year end 2003, had twelve producing Wolfberry wells, five in the Sweetie Peck venture with Entre, and seven in the WCJV prospects with Pure. The count kept climbing. Dave Feavel vowed to fund an ice cream float office party when the total Wolfberry rate hit a sustained 1000 BOPD. He made good on his promise in March 2004.

Bill was leasing as fast as Dave was mapping, and he and his team secured the remaining available large acreage blocks in the WCJV a few months later. There remained smaller blocks of acreage available within "the Big Line," but Dave and his geologists were already mapping outside the WCJV box. He recalled the blitz: "When I was putting in eighty-hour weeks, Michelle said to me once, 'If I didn't know you any better, I'd think you were having an affair.' And I said, 'I am—with the Wolfberry.' When you see the gold ring, and you *know* it's the gold ring, you turn it up a notch."

Henry and Pure decided to expand their WCJV arrangement to include the new areas Dave had mapped. The WCJV Expansion agreement was created in the early spring of 2004, with Henry increasing its ownership in the new project to 30% and Pure keeping the rest. The project was soon populated with prospects north of Sweetie Peck in southeast Ector County, southeast of Chickadee in Upton County, and a few way out in Tom Green County, near San Angelo.

Pure had an office in downtown Midland, and the partners met face-to-face every two weeks for updates and planning. Henry's agenda for the April 14, 2004 meeting focused on a particularly urgent concern: "Activity hampered by trying to stay under several radar screens." Rumors of the team's success was leaking.

Under the agenda heading "Competitor Analysis," the first bullet point reads:

Henry and Pure – WE'RE NUMBER ONE!!!!!!!! (at least so far)

There follows an assessment of potential competitors in the play. A few large companies were becoming bullish on the Permian Basin, among them EOG, Chesapeake and Pioneer. They were not apparently aware of the Wolfberry play, but were aggressively acquiring acreage on other fronts.

The partners also saw that a few smaller operators, including the two that had offset the Boultinghouse lease, knew something of the play in that vicinity, and were beginning to pick up on Henry's broader success. And Henry management was getting questions from their MIP partners. Particularly worrisome were two majors, both capable of pursuing large plays, whose people had begun asking Henry what they were so busy about.

Secrecy had been a priority since the completion of the first two wells, and by now Henry had established some protocol for keeping a lid on things. For filing official completion documents with the RRC, the company had adopted the perfectly legal practice of reporting each well's production rate on the first day it made oil, when the oil rate was generally low and the water rate high (as a result of the water pumped into the well during the frac.)

They also classified the producers in the Spraberry (Trend Area) regulatory field. The STA was established by the RRC in 1952. Initially, only the Spraberry interval could be completed in a producing well classified in this field. But during the intervening years, the RRC had modified the STA field rules to include the Dean and Wolfcamp Formations. Now, a well producing from any or all three of the formations could be classified in the STA, without the operator being required to name the specific zones. So, even though many of Henry's early Wolfberry wells were completed only in the Wolfcamp—heavy on the Wolf, easy on the Berry—they were able to classify them in a regulatory field mostly populated with Spraberry producers. Other operators could assume that Henry was still drilling primarily in the Spraberry, and the Wolfcamp powerhouse would escape notice: "Oh, that's just Jim Henry, a little ol' Spraberry driller."

But low initial rates and STA classification could not conceal the truth forever. Henry's monthly production data soon became public domain, and nothing could disguise that Henry was drilling a lot of wells, and making a lot of oil. Gary Pitts played the Spraberry card when the industry info reporters came snooping: "Someone from PI [Petroleum Information company] called and said, 'What in the world is Henry doing? You guys have turned Upton County's production curve from declining to inclining.' And I said, 'We're just doing the same old thing, just drilling Spraberry wells.'"

Dave Feavel quit attending his monthly luncheon with other local exploration managers: "Not because I couldn't keep my mouth shut, but because I didn't even want the question asked, 'What the hell are you guys doing?' Out of sight, out of mind."

By the time of the April 14 meeting with Pure, Henry and the partners had acquired 61,000 acres, with 760 potential drilling locations. "The play occurs in 10+ counties around the Midland Basin," they wrote in the meeting notes. "[It] probably covers 3000+ sections; if eventually developed on 80s [one well every 80 acres] it could turn into 25,000 wells being drilled."

The last item on the agenda is titled "Where do we go from here?" Henry recommended that the partnership "lease another 125 sections (1000 wells of development) in prime reservoir resource areas ahead of the above competitors so that more favorable lease terms can be achieved." Bill believed they could lease at an average cost of $175 per acre, for a total investment of $14 million.

But the partners now realized there was no reason to stop at the arbitrary boundaries of the Expansion area. If the play did extend around the entire perimeter of the basin, so then should the land grab. Henry and Pure drafted a be-all-end-all agreement. The Wolfcamp Explosion was made effective November 1, 2004, although the work had started during the summer. Its purpose was "to identify prospects for new leasing in corridors along the east and west flanks of the Central Basin Platform, Ozona Platform, Eastern Shelf and Northern Rim of the Midland Basin, and possible other areas." Effectively, the project reached around the rest of the Midland Basin. And into the Delaware Basin. And apparently everywhere else, too.

A special operations team was created to map the areas geologically and identify available land. The group comprised members from both Henry and Pure: Henry supplied Gary Pitts as the head, and geotech Vanessa Garner, and Pure loaned the team two geologists and a landman. Gary dubbed his team, "the Wolfpack." He created a special watermark for their documents, and every member got a custom team jacket. Gary and Vanessa moved to Pure's office for the duration of the project. Tony and Newt figured that, as Pure was the majority partner, funding two thirds of the Explosion project, they should have easy access to Gary. In return, Pure paid Gary's and Vanessa's wages. "Vanessa and I were usually there from about 6:30 a.m. to 7:00 p.m. each day," Gary recalled, "and as late as 1:00 a.m. the mornings before the meetings." The project ultimately yielded eighteen prospects, some way outside the main playground, ranging from Terry and Yoakum Counties in the north to Crockett in the south.

At the very beginning of the play, Henry adopted a regimen for assessing new prospects: they initially drilled two wells at each, so that the decision of whether to develop the area would be not determined by a single datapoint. They also spent whatever was necessary on these initial wells to evaluate the reserves potential definitively, to prevent nebulous results that might leave the team wondering whether the area was non-productive, or they had simply failed to conduct an effective test. They adhered to this regimen in all the Expansion and Explosion prospects. Sometimes, as with many of the outlier prospects, this practice painfully resulted in drilling two dry holes instead of only one. But at least it was definitive.

While they were poking exploratory holes in the play's frontier, Henry was also drilling excellent development wells in the established and expanding Chickadee and Sweetie Peck areas. Once they had proven that these areas warranted further development, they worked quickly to optimize all operational parameters—cost, logistics, schedules and timing, completion effectiveness—and began systematically drilling the 80-acre locations in "manufacturing mode."

It was during the Explosion phase that the "Wolfberry" moniker came to be. One day in early 2005, Gary was talking to Van about the technical aspects of the play. Gary recommended that, at least when communicating within the partnership, they call the play something other than "Spraberry Trend," because that is not what it really was. "Well, it's Spraberry and Wolfcamp, and Spraberry's the younger, so how about 'Spracamp'?" Gary suggested. Van grimaced, then offered the obvious alternative. It had a nice ring to it, and it stuck.

A few months later, Gary heard the nickname used in public for the first time, in a panel discussion at Midland's Executive Oil Conference. One of the men on the dais was a close friend, and Gary had discussed the play with him without requesting that he keep the nickname on the downlow. During the forum, the man offhandedly came out with it.

"Oh nuts," Gary said to himself, "we let that one out of the bag."

Henry had ended 2003 running three drilling rigs, two of them assigned to the Wolfberry. By April 2004, the rig count had grown to five, and by July it was eight. It jumped to ten in August, as two more crews were temporarily added to fulfill commitments at the Shafter Lake and Ackerly Dean waterfloods. The count then settled at eight for the rest of the year.

Since 1980, Henry had drilled an average of about twenty-five wells each year, running one to three rigs, on and off. The most wells the company had drilled in a single year was the anomalous forty-seven in 1984, all of them typical Spraberry wells. As Henry's rig count spiked in mid-2004 in response to Wolfberry lease obligations, the twelve-month drillwell tally shot up to 126, then averaged 135 for the next four years.

Henry was the proverbial dog that caught the bus. Regular drilling meetings became major events, as the number of attendees increased from just a handful to more than twenty. And they were held more often. During 2004, the meetings were held biweekly, with a revised rig schedule published after each. In 2005, the frequency increased to one per week, and each of them was, in Bill Fair's words, "critical—*painful*, but critical."

Henry's drilling rig roster was a dynamic lot, scrambled from companies then active in the Permian Basin. But the team also brought in some outsiders, including one from *way* outside. Sinopec is the world's largest petrochemical conglomerate, owned by the Chinese government and headquartered in Beijing. In the spring of 2006, Sinopec wanted to establish a physical presence in the US through its drilling subsidiary, DQG. Through an old Midland friend of Jim's, the Chinese group was introduced to Henry.

Henry management had significant concerns about DQG. The outfit had never drilled a well in the United States, and would use their own Mandarin-speaking crews (Doug Smith referred to them, with no disparagement intended, as "the Chinese boys"). Not to mention that they were ultimately run by a huge Communist government bent on world domination. But oil was trading between $70–75 per barrel, so drilling activity was high and rigs were scarce. And Jim saw potential for some cross-cultural goodwill.

Sinopec assembled and sent two rigs for the venture. One arrived at its assigned location at the JTL prospect, in southeastern Midland County. It moved in, rigged up, and spudded on April 20. The second was supposed to have spudded the same day, but it showed up in the Henry office parking lot. Fortunately, someone caught them before they broke ground. And as operations manager Ronnie Scott recalled, "That was about as good as it got."

Both rigs were outfitted with shoddy equipment. The language barrier proved insurmountable, especially over the phone, and translators were of little help. The crews' safety standards were a world away from Henry's, literally. Ronnie, Doug and Michael Rhoads (Henry's manager over drilling) worked with the crews to bring them up to spec, but to no avail. The two rigs drilled twenty-five wells between them during the course of eleven months, and a third rig showed up and drilled two more, before Ronnie finally terminated the contract due to safety concerns. "It was a very, very difficult experience. Usually time heals, but not that wound."

A second foreign invasion, this one from the north, was much more fruitful. Western Lakota Drilling of Calgary also wanted to enter the US market, and they already had experience in the States, having drilled wells in North Dakota and Montana. The company wanted a presence in the Permian Basin, and they contacted Henry around the same time Henry was beginning with Sinopec. Henry contracted two Lakota rigs in the summer of 2006. With no language barrier and a kindred view of safety, this was the beginning of a beautiful friendship, one that continued for many years and millions of feet.

Henry's selection of drilling rig contractors was not a low-bid process. The quality of the equipment and the experience and safety record of the crews mattered, because the Wolfberry could get wild. Henry's team got introduced to that wildness right at the start.

During the completion of the Beverly #1, when the well was being prepared for production following its frac, the completion foreman, who had years of experience but was new at Henry, left the wellhead open for a few minutes without any control equipment in place. That was a mistake. The well had not been flowing to that point, and there was no indication of pressure down below. But it suddenly erupted, disgorging a torrent of hot water and sand out of the hole and over the top of the derrick. There were a lot of people on location—the frac crew, the pulling unit crew, mostly young guys. Everyone scattered. For several minutes there was chaos. No one knew what to do. As Dennis Phelps remembered: "It was scary, really scary. I was afraid that if they didn't stop the water, the oil would start coming with it, then we're gonna burn the rig down…I was praying, because that's all I knew to do."

The foreman took action. "None of the young guys did anything. But this little 75-year-old man, the oldest, weakest-looking guy on location, grabbed the workover crew, and they got in there while it was blowing sand-laden water at pressures that had to be like standing in front of a fire hose, and they got the blowout preventer over the wellhead and torqued it down and shut her off."

This near disaster was the result of an error in judgment, but the Wolfberry could be difficult to control even when everything was properly done. The difficulty resulted from the difference in pressure between the two primary reservoirs. "The Permian Basin is a very docile area to drill," Doug explained. "But when the low-pressure Spraberry and the high-pressure Wolfcamp are open to the same wellbore, you got a problem."

The problem is that because the Wolfcamp has a high reservoir pressure, dense drilling fluid is necessary to prevent it from producing into the wellbore, or *kicking*, while the formation is being drilled. But the Spraberry above it has a low *fracture gradient* (little pressure is required to crack it) and consequently cannot hold a column of heavy fluid. If the Spraberry is inadvertently fractured while drilling in the Wolfcamp, the drilling fluid drains out of the wellbore into the Spraberry, and the force that was holding back the oil in the Wolfcamp subsides. When that happens, as Doug said, "It'll come to see you."

This is precisely what happened at the Norma #1 in June 2004, not quite a year into the play. The rig was drilling ahead at 9440 feet when it hit a *drilling break*—that is, the bit's rate of penetration increased suddenly, indicating that it had encountered a high-porosity zone. And because it was in the Wolfcamp, the zone was also high-pressured. Doug was on location: "It unloaded the hole from bottom to top in just a matter of minutes. And you could tell that when the oil hit the surface, it was gonna be a bad one." With no back pressure now on the Wolfcamp, the oil and gas would soon be exiting the wellbore at a high velocity and very difficult to control.

Several circumstances made the situation worse. The drilling rig on the Norma was not the best quality, as engineer Michael Rhoads recalled: "The crew couldn't mix and circulate mud to kill the well because of unreliable equipment; the pumps kept going down." The lease roads were muddy because it was raining hard, a rarity in the West Texas summer (or any other season, for that matter), and the heavy equipment needed for assistance kept getting stuck. And this was right before the 4th of July weekend, so many people were on vacation. Not to mention that they were at the Chickadee prospect in the boonies of central Upton County, a long way from help. "If there could be something going wrong, it was going wrong on this well," Michael said. All the while, "the oil and gas coming through the choke sounded like a jet engine. It blew out the back of the drilling pit because of the velocity of the fluid."

This situation on the Norma was not like that on Henry's Parham and Beverly wells. Those were actual *blowouts*, with fluid shooting out of the wellbore and into the sky whither it would. They were uncontrolled situations. But the Norma, as desperate as it sounds, was controlled. Doug had ensured that the rig was running proper blowout prevention equipment, and the crew was able to divert the oil into the drilling pits. The situation was not resolved, but it was under control.

And this was not Doug's first rodeo: "I made a pretty good bull rider in college." He also knew how to tame a wild well. Doug had been trained in well-control methods while at Exxon, and he brought that experience to Henry. To this point, he had not had much occasion to use it. But the Wolfberry now summoned it forth.

At the Norma, because of the extremely high permeability and pressure of the zone and the Spraberry's low fracture gradient, Doug's conventional methods were insufficient to kill the well. He and Michael drew up a few creative procedures to rectify the situation, but each one they attempted, Norma rejected. The battle continued for a week.

Finally, at the recommendation of a friend of Dennis Johnson, they conducted a modified version of what they called a "sandwich kill." The process basically entailed pumping two different kinds of fluid into the hole, one down the drill pipe and the other down the annulus, to create something like a shield across the Spraberry and protect it from being fractured by the dense fluid used to hold back the Wolfcamp. The procedure required an enormous volume of fluid, so Doug scavenged every holding tank in the county and spent a day and a half trucking brine water to the location while the well continued to spew.

They pumped the sandwich kill on a Friday just after midnight, with Doug and Michael punch-drunk from lack of sleep. The procedure failed, but they were able to troubleshoot the design, and modified it accordingly. They began the second attempt late that afternoon. It was successful, and they regained full control of the well. No one hurt, no property damaged.

Doug had to reprise the sandwich kill several months later and three miles east, on the Caden lease in the Upland prospect. The Caden #1 was drilling ahead on a Friday before noon when the bit poked into a high-porosity zone at the base of the Wolfcamp. The well began kicking, and Doug was called out to location. "This one was worse than the Norma due to higher pressure. But we already had a sense of how the sandwich kill worked." As with the Norma, the well was properly equipped and the situation controlled. While the rig crew circulated heavy mud, Doug mustered the requisite army of water haulers and holding tanks to prep for the operation. The term "sandwich kill" appears in the daily report this time without any explanation—the team now knew the routine, and they conducted the kill successfully the next day. They then drilled on to TD and things remained calm—for a while.

On Saturday, the crew was cleaning out the borehole to prepare it for running casing. With the bit at 8600 feet, the well suddenly started to flow. They killed it in about two hours and continued cleaning out to bottom, where the well kicked again. This time they performed a mini sandwich kill and shut off the flow for the moment.

At some point along the way, when it became clear that the well was going to be a problem, Doug had called Roy Madison for assistance. Roy called Faye and requested a stuck-on-location bag with a couple changes of clothes. He was particular about the skivvies: "Pack the old underwear, not the new cartoon stuff you got me for Valentine's Day—if this gets out of hand and some hairy-legged EMT guy has to cut my jeans off, I don't want him to see 'I Love You' staring up at him from my backside."

The crew began running casing. They made it to about 7500 feet when the well started to flow again. To put it simply, a kick while running casing is a bigger problem than a kick while drilling, and it is particularly difficult to pull casing back out of the hole under these circumstances. But because the hole clearly required cleaning out with a bit, they had to retrieve the casing. The cleanout run took a day and a half, and the crew was very careful not to provoke the well. They managed to keep it slumbering while they pulled the bit, ran the casing, and cemented it. With proper equipment and responsible people in place, the Caden never got out of hand. Roy and his lingerie were safe.

The team also had to tame a wild well of a different color. In mid-November 2006, drilling was underway on a Wolfberry well headed for 10,200 feet, when the crew was surprised by a high-pressured kick not quite halfway down. They were in the Grayburg Formation, the same zone that seventy miles north and thirty-five years earlier had surprised a Henry crew at the Parham #1. But whereas the Grayburg at Phoenix produced oil, here in Upton County it made only nitrogen gas—inert and nonflammable, basically air minus the oxygen. It would not ignite and explode, but it was coming out of the ground at a dangerously high rate.

At first, Doug had the crew follow the standard procedure of pumping heavy mud down the drill pipe to kill the flow. The dense mud did little to impede the hemorrhaging, and they began choking back the gas to prevent it from producing so forcefully. But holding too much back-pressure on the Grayburg could break down a weaker zone above it, just as with the Wolfcamp-Spraberry problem. For a day, Doug and Michael let the well produce wide open, directing the gas off the location and out over the pasture (as the gas was basically air, this action did nature no harm). The formation did not draw down: after flowing twenty-four hours unrestricted through both chokes, the pressure dropped only ten pounds, from 600 to 590.

Two days later, Doug special-ordered kill fluid to location, and the team was successful in shutting off the flow. There was no question of drilling on to the planned depth, and they pumped cement plugs, abandoned the well and moved on. No injury or damage, but no Phoenix discovery this time either.

Michael credited Doug's creativity for Henry's success in Wolfberry well-control situations: "Not only did Doug do the right things, but he did the right things in a very unconventional way. Many of the situations we faced basically voided the assumptions that go into the standard well-control procedures you read about in a textbook. So you have to improvise and modify, you have to bring a lot of experience and common sense and creativity. A lot of sounding board, a lot of back-and-forth. And I know we all made a great team doing that."

Doug's acknowledgement of his contribution was, as usual, more to the point: "I kept Jim's name out of the newspaper."

———————

Geology kept mapping. Land kept leasing. Drilling kept drilling. And operations kept fracking wells and bringing them online. Henry's operated Wolfberry well count was growing at a fast clip. Between 2003 and 2006, the count increased from 12 to 311. The production climbed from 500 BOPD to 11,000. And this was in addition to the other few hundred wells and several thousand daily barrels at the company's existing projects.

Henry needed a bigger crew. In January 2003, a few months prior to the birth of the Wolfberry, the company's employee head-count stood at 63. Once the play kicked off, Henry began hiring. The 2004 company Christmas party invitation list, compiled at the end of the Wolfberry's first full year, included 83 employees, up a third from the year before. There were also 16 contractors, ten in the office and six in the field. By late 2006, the Christmas list was at 102 employees and 37 contractors. The population had swelled by two and a half times in four years. The question most commonly asked at company meetings was, "Who's that?"

There was one unforeseen, self-inflicted consequence of the company's Wolfberry success. Since 1985, in accordance with management consultant Walter Scott's advice, Jim and Dennis had allowed geologists, engineers, landmen and managers to participate with a working interest ownership in the company's projects. In oil and gas development projects, a working interest typically requires a significant outlay before much revenue is obtained. In a simple example, an owner buys a lease and pays for a well to be drilled, completed and equipped, all before any oil is produced. This up-front spending is referred to as "digging the capital hole." The revenue begins as soon as the well is producing, but it takes a few years to recoup the investment before the cashflow turns to profit. And when many wells are drilled in a short amount of time, the capital hole can become quite deep indeed.

During the early Wolfberry, many of Henry's employee investors were thirty- to forty-somethings, investing in company prospects to help pay for things like a house, kids' college tuition and retirement. Prior to this point in the company's experience, prospects did not come along very often, and employees generally took moderately high ownership to capitalize on the infrequent opportunities.

The Wolfberry play turned out to be very different, with new prospects secured all the time and offered to the employees as if on a conveyor belt. But in each instance, employees feared that the current opportunity might be the last, and they continued to sign up for moderate percentages. Most often, the initial prospect cost was only for the acreage, which required a relatively small outlay. Within a few months, the company would drill its routine first two wells in the prospect, more costly but manageable. But due to the excellent results at Sweetie Peck and Chickadee, those areas were soon in manufacturing mode, with two rigs planted at each, drilling away with abandon as new prospects kept coming in the door. The employees' JIBs (*joint interest billing*, the monthly bill for investments and expenses) quickly grew an order of magnitude, and continued to escalate uncomfortably into five (or more) figures. Most employees were not financially prepared for this pace, but by virtue of their ownership they were strapped onto the Wolfberry rocket with no exit till the end of the ride.

Jim and Dennis saw this happening. They wanted to keep the employees in the program, not only because their participation benefited the company as a whole, but because ownership had made Jim and Dennis wealthy, and they wanted that for their people.

So they assembled all the employee investors one day in March 2005. Comptroller Kim Harris took the floor like a preacher in a pulpit and decried the dangers of debt, exhorting everyone to abstain from borrowing if at all possible. He paused to allow his admonition to sink in. "Having said all that," he continued, "Henry has secured a $50,000 line of credit for each of you." The accounts were set up at Community National Bank under the auspices of Danny Campbell, who had joined the bank when he left CMS ahead of its acquisition by Perenco in 2002.

Arranged credit notwithstanding, the employees' JIBs had risen so high that what was intended as a blessing began to appear a curse. Even though they knew the pain would yield ultimate gain, they dreaded the monthly bills. Digital billing had not yet caught on at Henry, and each month, the accounting department printed hard copies of the JIBs for distribution. In prior days, Demetra Johns, Henry's accounting supervisor, would gather them in the crook of her arm and pass through the office, handing them out to the employees. But as the Wolfberry burgeoned, the JIBs came to be measured not in pages long but inches thick, and Demetra began pushing a library cart through the halls, loaded with the statements. The folks could hear her coming, not only by the rumbling of the cart, but by the anguished moans of their comrades receiving their bills ahead of them.

––––––––––––

During the first two years of their Wolfberry program, the relationship between Henry and Pure had borne much fruit and goodwill. Each team had adapted to the other's management style, and the two were now conducting business almost as a single entity.

But in April 2005, Chevron announced its intention to acquire Unocal, in a stock and cash transaction valued at $18 billion that included assets all over the world. That's a lot of money and faraway places. But as Pure was owned by Unocal, Chevron would be acquiring Pure as well. And who was this little company attached to Pure? Some family-owned shop in West Texas was spending a quarter of a billion dollars annually in something called the "WCJV Explosion," and two thirds of that was on Pure's bill. Chevron was about to be spending $180 million a year on drillwells operated by an outfit they had never heard of.

It was imperative for Henry's sake that Chevron slip right into Pure's seat at the WCJV table and continue participating in the program. If Chevron stepped on the brakes, or even tapped them, drilling deadlines would be missed and acreage lost. Henry management worried that Chevron would balk if Henry did not have a company safety program in place, complete with a bona fide safety manual. Ronnie assigned Steve Owen the daunting task. "I hated that job," Steve recalled, "but I learned a lot." At large companies, Steve had seen safety taken to extremes, where it became the end rather than a means. But he discarded his preconceptions, rolled up his sleeves and got to work. "I met a lot of good contract safety hands who were genuinely concerned about getting men home for dinner every day. They helped me understand that real safety is not stupidity, and they taught me to emphasize what's important. I learned a lot about OSHA and what they really expect, versus what some safety leaders think they expect." That wisdom is the fruit of humility, and Henry and its partners were the beneficiaries.

But it remained to be seen whether it would suffice for Chevron.

Chapter 13
Departures

IF THERE WERE a flaw in Henry's hiring practice since the 1980s—though it could hardly be called a flaw—it was that Jim and Dennis hired alphas like themselves, self-directed folks with the initiative and skills to run their own ventures. Henry's success since then had been largely a product of that practice. The MIPs, flips and floods were only possible because of such people, and the Wolfberry would certainly not have happened without them.

But there were bound to be departures, as the alphas grew into entrepreneurial maturity and determined that it was time to start their own show. In summer 2005, with the Wolfberry going strong and oil north of $60, the leaving began.

Chevron's acquisition of Unocal was successful, but not easy. Enticed by Unocal's Asian holdings, the Chinese National Offshore Oil Corporation launched a rival bid and actually offered more money. This provoked the US Congress to enter the conversation, wary of the Chinese government's increasing oil appetite and its potential control of a US company. China eventually withdrew their bid, and Chevron closed the deal on August 10, 2005. On the local front, Henry's operational track record and Steve Owen's safety manual convinced the major that the independent was a sound Permian partner.

On the sad side, the transaction broke up Henry's partnership with Tony Best and Newt Newton, although not completely and not forever. Tony withdrew into temporary retirement, and Newt was retained by Chevron as project manager of the Permian, which meant that he would be Chevron's liaison with Henry in the Wolfberry play.

But a problem surfaced during the due diligence period. At least a potential problem. And for Henry, a very big one. Chevron was about to slip into the passenger seat of Henry's Wolfberry express, which was spending at the rate of $20 million per month. Chevron knew almost nothing about the Wolfberry, and it would likely take time to get them comfortable with the play, and with Henry.

This likelihood alerted Henry management to a detail within the WCJV agreement that could stop the Wolfberry development program in its tracks. The drillwell AFEs that Henry, as operator, presented to the partnership for approval, were good for only ninety days. In other words, if a given well was not spudded within ninety days from the date that its AFE was signed by Henry's partner, then the approval was voided and that well could not be drilled as scheduled. At this time, the seven-headed rig monster was making ten holes a month, and Henry was cranking out a feast of AFEs every few weeks to feed it. Pure had been readily signing them, so the partners had about two months of approved AFEs in the queue at any given time. Henry's managers figured it would take Chevron six months to get up to speed and begin approving AFEs, resulting in a four-month lag in activity. Chevron did have the option to *non-consent* AFEs—that is, they could decline to join the wells. But in that case, Henry would assume 100% ownership of the prospects where the wells were proposed. Given the play's success, Jim and Dennis would have been happy to increase Henry's ownership, but not by taking advantage of a partner, and not to the tune of 100%—the financial obligation would require Henry to take on more debt than Jim would allow.

"I have an idea," Dave Feavel told Dennis Johnson. "Let me go talk to Newt."

Dave laid out the issue for Newt, and Newt of course understood its significance. "What is Chevron allowing you to do during this interim?" Dave asked. Newt replied, "They're allowing me to honor existing commitments." "So can we change the process now, to where an AFE is authorized for 180 days instead of 90 days? That will give you time to get Chevron on board for the play, and it'll give us time so we're not laying down rigs." "Yes," Newt said, "I think we can do that."

Problem solved. The Henry team quickly scheduled wells and drafted AFEs to cover the next six months. Newt signed them for Chevron, and Henry and Newt worked determinedly to get Chevron up to play speed by the time a new batch of drillwell AFEs was needed.

Dave's resolution of the matter ensured the success of the Henry-Chevron partnership going forward. He knew as he worked out the arrangement that he would have nothing to gain from it materially: before the acquisition was even announced, he had privately made plans to leave Henry for his own venture. But no matter to Dave—he was happy to help his friends. "That was like my going away present to Henry."

On the morning of August 5, a few days before Chevron's Unocal acquisition closed, Dave Feavel, Mike LaMonica and Doug Robison rocked the Henry world by resigning. They were leaving to start an oil operating company of their own, which they named ExL Petroleum.

Jim understood, of course. The three were simply acting upon the same entrepreneurial urge that had prompted him to form his company. And Jim wanted them to succeed, even though ExL would soon be competing with Henry. "They were all friends of mine. They were going to start like I started. It was going to be difficult, and I was wishing them the best."

The ExL exit went smoothly, all things considered. There was one notable difference of opinion at the outset, but this was an almost inevitable consequence of such a parting. The two companies have continued as friends, and only sometime corporate competitors.

Jim and Dennis enacted a necessary reorganization in response to the departure. Some of the change was merely titular, with "vice president" replacing "manager." But some very real responsibilities were condensed in accord with the smaller management team. Ronnie Scott, who had been production manager, absorbed Mike's responsibilities and became VP of operations and engineering. Gary Pitts added Dave's geology to his responsibilities, and became VP of exploration and business development. Kim Harris was promoted from comptroller to CFO and VP of finance. And Bill Fair, who had been over the land group as manager, was now VP of land. Dennis remained president and COO, and Jim maintained his role as chairman and CEO.

In the summer of the next year, June 2006, Tony Best emerged from semi-retirement and joined St. Mary Land and Exploration as president and COO, determined to establish a presence in his old playground, the Permian Basin. At the time, Henry was about to start shopping for a partner at its new Halff East prospect in Upton County. By now, with the play proven and its financials more certain, Jim and all of management were in agreement to rachet up Henry's ownership. They determined to retain 40% at Halff East and were looking for a partner to carry the balance.

At his new post with St. Mary, Tony was the obvious call. He even knew the prospect, as the Henry-Pure WCJV had drilled wells adjacent to it in one of the most prolific areas of the play. Tony brought his St. Mary team to Henry's office, but the meeting was almost a formality: St. Mary was in, the deal was done, and the partnership immediately spudded the first prospect well.

Tony's reunion with Henry was a benefit to both parties at the Halff East prospect. But his intention to increase St. Mary's Permian presence on a larger scale would, in a few months, yield a financial bounty many times greater than Henry had ever known.

By late 2006, Henry's inaugural Wolfberry prospect, Sweetie Peck, was three and a half years old. Henry had proven the extent of the prospect by drilling 61 wells, but there were plenty of remaining interior locations. Henry's non-operating partner in the prospect, Entre Energy Partners, was headed by private equity pioneer Jeff Sandefer. Jeff's plan from the beginning had been to drill enough wells to *prove up* (validate) the oil potential of the property, and then market it to larger operators as a best-of-both-worlds opportunity: cash flow from existing production alongside remaining drillable locations. (This strategy would become the private equity model of choice later in the 2000s.)

As a critical part of the Sweetie Peck arrangement, Henry had agreed to sell along with Jeff when he determined the time was right. With Henry, as operator, also selling, the partners hoped to receive the *operator premium*—the markup paid in such transactions by buyers who want to operate themselves, and thus control the pace of development (a non-operating partner often has little say in such matters). Now, with the prospect proved up, drillable locations remaining and oil in the $60–70 range, Jeff was ready to sell.

As Henry was preparing to market the property, Tony got wind of the sale. He conducted a quick evaluation of Sweetie Peck, and flew down from Denver to personally hand Dennis Johnson a pre-emptive bid. Tony's bid was too low, and Dennis countered with his buy-it-now price of $250 million. When Tony said he could not go that high, Dennis stood fast: "I'm sorry, but that's what our working interest owner group has set as its minimum price, $250 million—and not a dollar less." They were at an impasse. Tony left to catch his return flight, but an hour later, he called Dennis from the airport and asked to meet him at a local restaurant. Dennis described this conversation as one of his happiest moments at Henry: "As we sat across the table over a Coke, Tony said, 'OK, I'll do $250 million—*and not a dollar more!*' And I said, 'Deal!' We shook hands, and my heart literally jumped in my chest. This meant so much to Henry and all our employees' futures!"

That was an understatement. Henry's take was about a third of the sale price, the largest cash-out in the company's thirty-seven-year history. Owing to Jim and Paula's policy of sharing their gain with the people who gained it for them, it was a fantastic win for the employees, yielding bonuses above their annual salaries. Erstwhile vocational education student Laurie Richards, who had experienced many bonus events during two and a half decades with the company, had never dreamed of anything like this. "The Sweetie Peck sale was when things got wow-crazy. I remember we were all, like, *'Holy Moly!'*" Every employee in the company—top to bottom and side to side—received a proportionate share. The blessing of Good Providence through Jim and Paula is particularly apparent in the case of the field employees, who four years earlier were contractors with no benefits. They had been hired shortly before the first Wolfberry completion in 2003, and now, along with everybody else, they were showered by fallout from the Henrys' generosity explosion. The employees with a participating interest in the prospect got a double payday, as they were able to sell their interests to St. Mary at a price proportional to that paid to Henry.

———

On the last day of January the following year, Gary Pitts was leaving to attend the winter North American Prospect Expo in Houston. As Henry's head of business development, Gary always attended the NAPE conventions. But this year, on his way out the door, he announced that when the conference was over, he would not be returning. He had decided to throw in with his friends Tony and Newt in St. Mary's new Midland office, to assist them in acquiring properties and growing the company.

Two weeks later, Van Temple made the same trek. St. Mary was just taking over operations from Henry at Sweetie Peck, and as Van had worked the prospect from its inception, he believed he could help his friends continue its successful development. Van's leaving was particularly hard because of his role as Henry's unofficial chaplain: he counseled the cohort wisely and challenged them kindly, all the while suffering with an intractable illness. He was, as several of his coworkers said, "one of those very special people you very seldom meet."

There had been a lot of leaving in a short amount of time. The ExL exodus eighteen months earlier had already left Henry three managers down. "And then when Gary left," Ronnie said, "this was an *oh dang!* moment—now we're down *four* managers. And then two weeks later Van left—now we're down *five!* And now the community started asking, 'What's wrong at Henry?'"

A much bigger leave was already in the works.

Early on the Monday morning of February 19, 2007, four days after Van's departure, Jim and Dennis summoned the office to a mandatory meeting. Everyone knew something big was up. When they arrived at the conference room, the writing was literally on the wall—a large banner, reading "Summit Petroleum, Best Wishes on Your Exciting New Adventure." Dennis and his son, Matt, who had joined Henry as an engineer in 2003, were leaving to start their own operating company.

On a morning during the previous week, Dennis had collected Ronnie and taken him to Jim's office. He shut the door and gave them the news. As previously explained, Jim had arranged for Dennis to earn equity in the company over a period of time, and by now Dennis owned roughly a quarter interest. So, while Jim had not known Dennis's timing, he was not surprised by his announcement. "As soon as we were successful at Henry, he would leave. We both knew that he would leave, and we had talked about it." Nor was Jim deeply anxious about all the recent departures: "No, I don't think it really worried me too much. We *lost* some really good people, but we also *had* some really good people."

During his address to the gathered, Dennis explained the decision to leave. The timing, he said, was a little ahead of his plan, but Gary and Van had manned important posts in Henry's corporate structure, and the company would now have to make critical decisions about reorganizing and hiring. As Dennis and Matt would have been leaving soon in any case, they wanted to spare Henry the turmoil of a second major reorganization.

The actual splitting process was complicated. The company was in the middle of the Wolfberry blitz, running nine rigs and completing about twelve wells every month. Lease obligations had to be met and the drilling must continue, so contracts were separated and consultants reassigned on the fly. And as Chevron had to approve parts of the transaction, all of the AFEs, operating agreements and assignments had to be separated between Henry and Summit without violating any terms of the WCJV. By virtue of his arrangement with Jim, Dennis was allowed to make job offers to about a quarter of Henry's employees, commensurate with his ownership. Dennis and Ronnie, whom Jim had appointed to represent Henry's side in the negotiation, had to be very careful about who went where, because "in all respects, Chevron had to be convinced that both companies were viable and could operate Chevron's interests properly." The two parties successfully concluded the negotiation in only seventy days, and, according to Ronnie, "We were Christians for about sixty-four of them. It was often tense, but not angry, as family deals can be. Everyone was very gracious and patient under the circumstances."

Jim and Dennis, Henry and Summit, parted ways and proceeded down their separate paths, still as friends. Although Dennis had been allowed to hire twenty-five of Henry's employees, he only hired ten, because, he said, "I wanted to ensure that Jim and the remaining employees at Henry could be certain to maintain a strong and capable company." At Dennis's request, Ronnie presented Summit's reserves to Summit's new lending bank for the first year. Ronnie best knew the valuation details, as he had stewarded the properties when they were all in Henry's shop, and he was happy to help Dennis. Henry still retains a non-operated working interest in some of Summit's properties. And Henry and Summit technical teams participate in a quarterly, informal consortium with a few similarly minded companies, sharing experiences, plans and suggestions for developing the horizontal Wolfberry in the Midland Basin.

And here is continuing goodwill, on all sides.

Employees who were with Henry during those departure times speak of "the Henry cousins," the companies formed or headed by ex-Henry employees. This is not at all belittling, but it is a familial term, an acknowledgement of a common bloodline. A cousin is not a clone. The corporate personalities of Henry, Summit, ExL and the rest are notably distinct, with different organizational structures and strategies, inhabiting different industry niches. But they have a shared spirit, a common core of character, excellence and goodwill. So they are cousins, not twins, but the family resemblance is unmistakable.

This is not to suggest that the men who formed these second-generation companies learned the Henry Way from Jim, and transplanted it in their own soil. That would be to conflate the effect with the cause. It is true that Henry is what Henry is because Jim and Paula built it on their priorities. But Henry has remained what Henry is because Jim and Dennis and the other managers hired like-souled men and women who already had the same priorities. Together at Henry, iron sharpened iron, and they all challenged each other to improve individually and as a company.

As Dave and Dennis and Mike and the others helped to preserve and improve Henry while they were here, their experiences at Henry improved them. They have continued the process in their own companies. "Who I am today at ExL Petroleum is a result of my time at Henry," Mike said. "I try to take the best of what I learned at Henry and apply it to the new company." Mike and Dave and Doug have now receded into advisory roles at ExL, but when they were managing the company, they, too, created a bonus program similar to Henry's. "And when we did good," Mike said, "every single person, down to the receptionist, everybody made money." At Summit, Dennis practices the same generosity that he experienced and promoted at Henry: "Laquita and I try to be a river that passes the Lord's blessings along to others." To that end, he established an incentive compensation program and an employee participation arrangement similar to those he helped design at Henry.

The members of the Henry management fraternity, ex and present, remain friends. This is not to say that they all love hanging out together. They are leaders with leader personalities, and they want things run their way—hence the departures. There are a few personality pairings within the group that are best kept infrequent. But there is sincere, mutual appreciation for what each received from the other, and for what they accomplished together at Henry. As Mike described it, "Henry felt like one big family, you cared about each other." Even though there were significantly different opinions and personalities? "Yes, that's what made it work." "We had a great bunch of people all set on one thing," Gary Pitts said of his time at Henry. "Everyone pretty well kept their egos in check, and we all worked together to make Henry grow and be prosperous."

Departures created some meaningful holes in Henry's organization chart over those eighteen months. Henry had about 100 employees before the leaving began. Dennis's exit increased the empty manager slots to six, leaving only three filled: Ronnie, whom Jim appointed the new president, Bill Fair over land and Kim Harris over finance. Ten staffers had elected to join Dennis at Summit, and a few others had also exited, leaving holes in the lower echelons as well. Henry now had some 80 souls to manage a 100-soul Wolfberry program. The company needed to reload. And in the wake of many tough departures, Henry soon had some welcome arrivals.

Danny Campbell had by now intersected Henry a few times, first in the CMS dealing when he gave Gary Pitts the heads-up that turned out to be the Wolfberry portal, and later at Community National Bank as Henry's established lender for the employee owners in the play. On the same day that Dennis announced his leaving, Ronnie called Danny, largely on the recommendation of Bill Fair and Kim Harris. As Danny recalled, "I thought he wanted to talk about property values, because as Henry's past banker I knew some of the details of the early agreement between Jim and Dennis." Danny was mistaken. Ronnie wanted to hire him. Paula and Jim were elated at Danny's coming to the company, and they knew the move would quell the community rumor mill. "When we hired Danny Campbell," Jim said, "this told Midland we weren't going away." Danny joined Henry in May 2007, as VP of business development.

Later that year, Henry raided Oxy to refill the engineering ranks and picked up the Bledsoe brothers, Billy and David, both homegrown Midlanders and Permian Basin veterans. The pair joined Henry as staffers on the same day in August 2007. Henry conducted a second Oxy raid a few months later, in January 2008, this time to replenish the geology slots. They hired veteran geophysicist Craig Corbett as VP of exploration, not for his prowess in fracking with giant sticks of dynamite, but for his experience in prospecting and dealmaking.

All four of these men played key roles in perpetuating Henry's success after the previous leaders left, with each moving the company forward in his own niche. Craig pointed Henry into a new play, when it became clear that the Wolfberry was winding down. Billy was later promoted to manager of operations, where he cultivated a closer, more effective relationship between the field and office staffs than Henry had previously known. And Danny and David wound up running not a part but the whole of Henry as co-managers of the entire enterprise: David with his business development skill over the oil company, and Danny with his finance expertise over the diversified investments.

These men are kindred spirits and were seamlessly sewn into the Henry fabric. And they arrived just in time for a financial blessing that the little ol' Spraberry driller of yesteryear could not have imagined.

Chapter 14

Concho

At Jim's decree after Dennis's leaving in February 2007, Ronnie Scott became the COO and third president of Henry Petroleum. "Dennis had kind of groomed Ronnie to take his place," he said, "so we weren't going to be in a bind."

Ronnie began his term by assessing all aspects of Henry's current situation. Due to the Summit split, the asset tally was now leaner by a quarter, but there was still plenty of undeveloped acreage to drill. Henry was operating 900 wells and producing 19,000 BOEPD (both figures gross), and the numbers were steadily increasing, with the Wolfberry program still in high gear. The rate of new acreage adds had slowed but not stopped, and the company was steadily developing its high-potential areas in central Upton and southern Midland counties. The pace was fast but not furious. Oil was in a comfortable range at 60 bucks a barrel.

Ronnie saw all these nuts and bolts, but he also contemplated the existential situation: in light of the tremendous growth at every level over the last four years and the recent departures, who was

Henry now? More importantly, who did Jim and Paula want it to be?

To answer these questions, Ronnie saw that Henry needed a comprehensive business plan, an omnibus database to compile the company's producing properties along with schedules and valuations for the remaining drillable locations. Before that time, Henry had planned the development schedule only out to a year and a half, and included only the *proven* locations (those offset by existing producers) that would be drilled within that timeframe. Consequently, the existing plan could not be used to assess the company's total value.

Ronnie determined to change this rubric and include *all* remaining drilling locations—not just the proven locations, but also the *probable* and *possible* (less-certain and lower-valued properties), regardless of when they would be drilled. He wanted to forecast Henry's capital spending, expenses and revenue over a much longer timeframe, to assess future capital and manpower needs and, most importantly, to determine a more accurate corporate valuation.

To create such a plan, Ronnie would have to answer a very important question: were 40-acre Wolfberry locations profitable? In compliance with the regulatory rules for the Spraberry Trend Area field, Henry had been developing the Wolfberry on 80-acre locations; that is, the wells were drilled 80 acres apart. This spacing had for years been considered adequate for draining the Spraberry formation. But the drainage characteristics of the Wolfcamp, particularly in the basin-rimming Wolfberry play area, were unknown. And given the scattered, unpredictable occurrences of its prolific detrital blocks, it was possible that significant oil reserves could yet be found in between the 80-acre locations. None of the growing throng of Wolfberry competitors had attempted a 40-acre program, so no one knew whether such wells could be profitable. In late spring, with work underway on the massive development forecast,

Ronnie and the technical team set about planning 40-acre test projects at Chickadee and Sweetie Peck.

In September, with the omnibus plan nearing completion, Ronnie commenced to mull its ramifications. What he saw was a huge number of drilling locations, an impending employee shortage, and a long time on the Wolfberry treadmill—ten years running eight rigs at least. Two things were certain: "If oil goes to $200, we're all good, but if it drops to $35, we're sunk." He considered this conclusion against the backdrop of Jim and Paula's essential priorities, which he framed in terms of risk management: protect the family business and protect the employees.

"I took a step back and thought about it," he recalled, and then he had an epiphany of his own: "It's a good time to sell."

The upside of a sale was obvious: cashing out would remove years of risk from the business plan, and the proceeds could be redeployed any number of ways to fortify the Henrys' financial future. One downside was equally obvious: the action would directly violate one of Jim and Paula's prime directives: don't sell the company.

Maybe there were alternatives for taking chips off the table, something other than an outright sale? Ronnie asked Danny for options, and Danny laid them out: IPO, equity sell-down, merger and outright sale. They discussed the merits of each. In the end, Ronnie saw that selling would best address the Henrys' top priorities: it would protect the family business by materializing the family's wealth—"fair market value" is wispy wealth, but cash is spendable—and it would protect the employees, by giving them a share of the cash through the bonus program.

Henry Petroleum was structured as a *C corporation*, or C corp; the *C* identifies the subchapter of the IRS code which governs the federal taxation of corporate entities. As per the code, the sale of a C corp's *assets* is taxed at a high rate, but the sale of the entire *company* is taxed at a lower rate. Henry Petroleum would have to be sold intact and outright—everything in one bundle, with no cherry-picking. If they sold, Henry would be saying goodbye to the new Wolfberry rock-star prospects right along with long-standing stalwarts: Shafter Lake, Pegasus, both Ackerly floods, Jim's remaining Spraberry wells—all of them would go.

A sale would mean saying goodbye to partners as well, among them Tony Best and Newt Newton, who had been collaborators and allies since 1992, spanning four different majors and several large projects, including the Wolfberry. Henry would lose its tie to ExxonMobil, which had been successful for both partners at the Pegasus FMEA since 1998, as well as its link to the Chevron team, who had been good friends since their acquisition of Unocal/Pure in 2005.

Perhaps the most poignant goodbye would be to the company name. "Henry Petroleum" was iconic in the Permian Basin in both industry and community circles. The company's reputation for integrity and accomplishment had landed Jim an untold number of speaking engagements through the years, and wherever he spoke, there was a placard or poster or screen somewhere on the stage bearing the company name. The name was also on sponsor pages in performing arts programs, fences around sports stadiums, signs at school science fairs and banners at just about every local fundraising event. With a sale, the time-trusted name of Henry Petroleum would be no more.

Ronnie considered all of this, adjusted his recommendation accordingly, and set up an initial presentation for Jim and Paula in early October. Ronnie and accountant Terry Creech laid out the benefits and clarified the ramifications of a sale. In the first place, the Henrys' oil company was not going to end. True, they would sell all of Henry Petroleum as a company, but in the process, they would create a new company into which they could place other assets and opportunities. As Ronnie described it, Henry Petroleum held about 80% of the Henrys' total oil and gas assets (Jim and

Paula had a few additional holding entities), and the remaining 20% could be used to grubstake the new enterprise. And the Henry name would be included in the title of the new company.

Importantly, this new company would be organizationally much smaller. Henry Petroleum had grown larger than Jim and Paula ever envisioned. With more than 120 people on the payroll, the company no longer had the family feel that the Henrys treasured. A sale would reduce the organization to 20–30 employees, as the other hundred would go with the assets to the buyer. The new Henry company could maintain the corporate personality that Jim and Paula preferred, and once again they would know all the employees and their spouses by name.

Ronnie knew that the welfare of their employees would be paramount in Paula and Jim's consideration of a sale. He explained that they would share the cash-out with the employees through the bonus plan. Assuming they could get a purchase price reflective of the company's revised valuation, the bonuses would be huge, and they would be paid to all employees, regardless of whether they went with the buyer or stayed at Henry. And to protect the employees' jobs, Ronnie and Danny would not sell auction-style, but would pursue a private, arranged sale only with companies that would retain the employees and treat them well.

Finally, Ronnie explained that a sale would allow the Henrys to restructure their estate, which they had been wanting to do. They could set up a stock ownership plan for their children, and arrange perpetual funding for The Henry Foundation, which they had created two years earlier. And with a liquidation, they could take the much-needed action of diversifying their investments, a big step toward securing their goals for the estate.

Jim and Paula didn't say yes, but they didn't say no. They wanted to proceed cautiously, with more dialogue. "I remember that meeting," Jim said. "I had always said we will never sell our company, so this was a very new concept to me. But I respected

Ronnie for bringing the idea to me." This was actually not the first time Jim had thought about a sale: "I had noticed that the people who *sold* their companies did better than the people who just *kept* their companies. When we were drilling the Chalk in the 80s, I saw a man do this, and he made out quite well."

Ronnie and Terry continued the dialogue during the next few weeks. Terry suggested that Jim call Henry Groppe, his oil price guru, and get his perspective on future price performance. Groppe confirmed to Jim that a big price drop was indeed possible, and he explained what that would mean for the company if it transpired. The Henrys' primary reluctance to sell was due to their concern for the welfare of the employees. "The people issues were big with Paula and Jim," Danny said, "always have been, always will be." But in the light of Groppe's response, Jim and Paula now saw that a sale might be the best way to protect and provide for their people. More than the collection of pros and cons regarding a sale, the factor that in the end convinced them was the consensus of their trusted advisers: "It was the quality of the men advocating it—the whole management team," Jim explained. "We realized that there were more for this than against it."

In early December 2007, Jim and Paula gave Ronnie their go-ahead—with qualifications. As Danny recalled, "A lot of it [their list of qualifications] was related to the employees. Jim and Paula wanted the buyer candidates to be companies that would hire all the people and keep them in Midland."

By this time, the team had gathered enough data to support the inclusion of 40-acre locations in the business model. The results were admittedly early, but the initial producing rates were very similar to those of the 80-acre wells, and the team concluded that 40-acre wells would be profitable. Ronnie loaded the 40-acre locations into the business plan, and then it really was omnibus. The resulting increase in the company valuation was, as anticipated, enormous.

———————

Once they received the Henrys' nod, Danny and Ronnie together determined the minimum acceptable sale price and devised a first draft of suitable buyers. Danny brought to bear his banking skills in deeply vetting the financial situations of these candidates, in order to cull the unfit: "High-grading was critical, so I spent a lot of time at it. I didn't want a last-minute discovery to cause the deal to fall through." His final shortlist included six companies.

Concurrently, Jim and Paula and their managers established the go-forward company, which would hold new assets picked up during the sale process. They named the entity Henry Resources, and structured it as a limited liability corporation, having recently learned a valuable C-corp lesson. The fourth incarnation of the Henry oil company was now up and running, although only upper management knew its ultimate purpose.

Ronnie and Danny hit the road with their sale show, meeting with all six suitors before the end of December. In each show, Ronnie was the primary presenter with Danny on hand to address finance questions. To keep the matter secret, they arranged all the presentations at remote, discreet sites. They conclaved for one showing in a hotel room in Dallas that Danny described as "like a scene from a spy movie."

The initial offers were lower than acceptable. Then, in February, one of the suitors submitted a number worthy of additional dialogue. Discussions ensued, and Ronnie negotiated the buyer to a point at which "the price was right," but he felt the environment was not quite right for the employees. He took this information to Jim and Paula: "If they're not going to take care of the employees," they responded, "don't sell."

At the end of February, with all identified candidates shown and subsequently scratched, the team dropped the sale effort for the moment. Plenty of other issues required their attention. The company was running nine rigs, and Ronnie needed to finalize his 2008 budget.

But in late March, an investment banker engaged by one of the scratched-off candidates called Danny: "Will you show Henry one more time?" "Probably not," Danny said. "We and Jim and Paula are all tired—the sale process was a little hard on everyone mentally and emotionally, and we're moving on." The banker persisted: "You know the party, you know them well, and we think you should show it one more time."

After some back and forth, the banker came clean: the entity was Tim Leach and Concho Resources. He had not told Tim about the opportunity, and he wanted Danny's authorization to bring Concho and Henry together. Danny had vetted Concho at the beginning of the process, he explained, but they had gone public only a short time earlier, and he figured they would be unable to borrow sufficient capital for the acquisition. The banker countered that Concho's stock price had since improved, and their credit base along with it. Danny updated his evaluation, and confirmed that Concho now had the wherewithal to complete the transaction. He passed this on to Ronnie, who took it to Jim and Paula. They all agreed that one more showing was worth a shot.

Before proceeding, Danny suggested an important change in the drilling schedule they had been showing to potential buyers as the basis for Henry's valuation. The schedule had originally been devised to serve as Henry's in-house budget forecast, so it reflected Henry's priorities. When the initial decision had been made to move forward with the sale effort, the schedule was conscripted into service without much repurposing. Specifically, the existing schedule favored locations with a fairly low rate of return but a high Henry interest, as Ronnie was focused on increasing the company's net ownership of its combined assets in the near term. Consequently, many higher-return but lower-interest wells were placed later in the drilling schedule. Danny wanted the schedule to reflect a buyer's priority of high rate of return, by moving those wells to the front of the schedule.

Ronnie rearranged the schedule accordingly, and made some modifications of his own. When they ran the revised model, they found that it yielded not only a higher rate of return, but a higher valuation as well. Danny now asked Ronnie for a bottom-line sale price based on the new valuation. "$560 million," Ronnie told him. "OK," Danny said, "I think I can get $560, but we'll have to take a little bit different negotiating tactic with Tim." Danny had worked for Tim Leach at Parker & Parsley. "I knew Tim inside and out, and he knew me inside and out. I had a strategy that I thought he would appreciate."

In early April, Ronnie and Danny, Tim and his Concho team, and the investment banker convened on the downlow at the CEED building between Midland and Odessa. To avoid notice, they slipped in and out at different times—more spy movie stuff. Ronnie delivered the technical presentation, then turned it over to Danny, who began by summarizing the terms of the sale: "Concho will buy Henry Petroleum with all its assets for $560 million. Henry will keep the cash on the company's books on the effective date, about $40 million. Concho will take about 100 employees and will supply them with jobs in Midland."

Then he explained the terms of the negotiation: "One dollar less than $560 million and Henry goes home, one dollar more and Concho goes home. You won't be making a bid—you'll just be deciding whether this number is OK." Danny had seen Tim use this same yes-or-no format himself. Ronnie gave Tim his deal deck and the omnibus development database, and Tim asked for a couple of weeks to consider.

As part of their evaluation, the Concho team asked their third-party auditor, CGA, for their assessment. "It's my understanding," Danny said, "that when CGA got through, they were within 1% of the value Henry had represented." So in late May, after five weeks of Henry waiting, Tim called.

"OK," he said, "I'm interested."

As the venue for negotiating the purchase and sale agreement—once again, in secret—the parties decided on the posh offices of Concho's outside counsel in downtown Houston. The first meeting was on Wednesday, May 28. Danny and Terry were involved with pressing matters in Midland, so Ronnie took Bill Fair and Kim Harris with him. Tim Leach brought two of his Concho cohort from Midland, and each party had retained three Houston attorneys. Concho's attorneys were very professional, well-suited and coiffed, what Bill Fair called "tall building lawyers." On the other side of the table, Ronnie, no slave to fashion himself, was chagrined to see that "two of our attorneys were old guys in green blazers." And while Concho's group was exchanging clearly well-acquainted greetings—"Is Hunter still quarterbacking for Rice?" "Give my love to Babs!"—Henry's team was just as clearly meeting for the first time: "Hi, my name is Ronnie. I work at Henry Petroleum. What's your name?" The Concho men were cordial and gracious, not at all condescending, but the event was a bit embarrassing anyway. Ronnie likened it to an episode of *The Beverly Hillbillies*.

By close of business on Friday, the parties had agreed on incremental price adjustments, with other terms still undecided. They decided to break for the weekend, and the Henry team flew home to Midland. The discussion resumed in Houston the following Monday, June 2. This time Danny and Terry came with Ronnie, which required more first-time introductions in front of the Concho team.

The negotiation pressed forward, and on Wednesday it was clear that the parties would reach a full agreement. As a publicly traded entity, and thus governed by the SEC in such matters, Concho determined to make the announcement the next day, June 5, after the market closing bell. Ronnie and Jim decided to announce the sale to the employees earlier the same day, to ensure that everyone at Henry got the news from them and not from the media. Ronnie flew back to Midland to make arrangements, while Danny and Terry remained in Houston and stayed up all Wednesday night fine-tuning the PSA with the Concho team. They finalized terms in the wee hours and boarded a red-eye back to Midland, bearing the docs for Tim and Jim and Paula to sign.

The total negotiation of the $600 million deal had taken only a week and a day. And a night.

———————

At the same time the negotiation was proceeding, Ronnie and the managers had begun dividing Henry's employees into two groups—those who would stay with Henry, and those who would go to Concho. The Henrys and Ronnie wanted both companies to have good people and to succeed. As Jim put it, "We weren't trying to select the best [to remain with Henry]. We wanted to be fair about it. We strongly believe in a win-win situation. Because if it's win-win, you can come back again. But if it's win-lose, you really don't want to deal with those people again." In some ways, this was the same song, second verse, of the Summit split, and that negotiation prepared Ronnie for this one.

Tim and the Concho team had not merely agreed to take on a share of Henry's employees—they positively wanted them. With funds raised by its IPO the previous year, Concho had acquired properties from Mack Chase in New Mexico, but had not retained any of that company's workforce. Now, Concho would need staff for the Henry properties as well, and Tim wanted assurance that Henry's people would stay with him.

Jim and Ronnie structured the Henrys' planned bonus payment to serve as an equitable solution. To give employees a strong incentive to stay with Concho, Jim and Paula would give them half of the total bonus up front, a quarter at the end of the first year, and the remaining quarter at the end of the second year. This arrangement provided incentive for the employees to stay at Concho for at least two years, which assured Tim that his staffing needs would be met. On the other side, if Concho terminated any Henry employees during the first two years, those people would receive their remaining bonus in full at that time. This gave the employees both bonus and paycheck security. (The employees who stayed with Henry would receive the entire amount up front, with the stipulation that if they left before two years, they must return a prorated amount. But there was no relative difference between the rewards received by the two groups.)

In the end, twenty-three people would stay at Henry, and a few more than a hundred would go to Concho.

On the morning of June 5, the day the announcement was secretly scheduled for release, employees showed up at the Henry building and started working as usual. At mid-morning, a small number of employees was summoned by Ronnie and the managers, privately and individually, to a meeting at Midland College's Advanced Technology Center. When each arrived and met their coworkers in the building, they found that none of them knew what was going on. They took their seats and speculated, but as soon as Ronnie started talking, there was perfect silence in the room.

Ronnie and Jim together announced the sale, and told the employees they would be sharing in the proceeds in a big way—"many times your annual salary," in Jim's words. Some would stay with Henry, and others would go with Concho. Those in the room would stay.

There were lots of emotions on lots of levels as the ramifications of the sudden surprise sank in. Big bonus, small company, friends staying, friends leaving. Long-timer Laurie Richards, whose relationship with the company was twenty-eight years strong at the time, said "I had no clue about the Concho sale coming. I remember crying in that meeting. I remember Steve Owen sitting beside me, hugging me, like, 'It's OK, it's OK.'" The employees were then dismissed, and enjoined not to talk about the news with anyone.

Shortly after lunch, Ronnie and Jim gave a second presentation in the same building, this time for all the employees, both those staying and those going. Notwithstanding their general dismay at not remaining with Henry, even those going to Concho gave Jim a standing ovation. One said to him, "I love you, Jim, but for that amount of money I'll happily leave you any day!"

The negotiation was concluded, and the announcement made, but the work of transition was only beginning. Concho got about their due diligence, and Henry set to making sure it went well. The company had been running fast for five Wolfberry years and had left some i's undotted and t's not crossed, particularly in the land shop. Bill cautioned the other managers that there was much work to be done in curing lease titles and transferring contracts: "Guys, we've been out there hunting, and we just shot 'em and threw 'em into the back of the truck. We got 'em. But they're not even field dressed, much less butchered."

Both companies pulled hard in the harness, and on July 31, only fifty-six days after the signing of the PSA, the transaction closed. The total cash Concho paid to Henry was $560 million, and Henry kept the $40 million cash in the company coffers. Henry's total purse was $600 million. Great wealth gotten.

The growth in Henry Petroleum's value is noteworthy. And amazing. At year-end 2002, right before the Wolfberry kickoff, the company's fair market value was $46 million. In April 2007, after Dennis left with his quarter, it was $185 million. Now, in August 2008, just eighteen months later, the company was worth more than $600 million.

Not bad for a little ol' Spraberry driller.

As they were closing the sale, Jim and Paula experienced a dawning realization: "It didn't become clear to us how wealthy we had gotten until we sold to Concho," Jim said. "We realized then that we'd hit the jackpot. Up to that time, we knew we were doing pretty good, but we weren't really wealthy." Well, they really were. But there's a tangible difference between ink on the books and money in the bank.

Jim and Paula responded to their getting of great wealth in perfect character—by giving away a lot of it. As planned, they gave first to their people: "We saw that we could give a lot of money to the employees that had been very faithful to our company and helped us get where we were," Jim said, "so the bonus program had been a big reason for selling." As always, in accordance with their bonus structure, every employee—from the top of the org chart to the bottom, in both the field and the office, whether staying at Henry or going to Concho—reaped the benefits of the sale. And Jim and Paula's generosity did not stop at employees. Some contractors and service providers who had been particularly helpful to Henry in the Wolfberry program were surprised to receive sizeable thank-you checks in the wake of the sale.

Jim personally distributed the bonuses to the employees who remained at Henry: "It's very rewarding to me to hand out that kind of money, because I've seen how it helps people, how it changes their lives." He always enjoyed seeing the employees' responses: "Of course, the girls cried, usually." A lot of people cried. Jim had not been exaggerating when he promised an amount many times their annual salary.

One of the "girls" who cried was Tara Sosa (then Marshall). Tara had been hired as a geotech three weeks before the announcement. Due to her short time, she was given a ratcheted-down version of the bonus, but it was "very meaningful" nonetheless. Tara had lost her parents a few years before, when she was still a teenager. She'd put herself through college on an athletic scholarship, supplemented with student loans. Her bonus was sufficient to clear all of her loans, and to pay for her wedding—Tara had gotten engaged the day after joining Henry. What was her response to the Henrys' generosity after working for them less than a month? "I cried. I cried forever. I still cry."

Notwithstanding that many would have chosen to remain at Henry, the bonus from Jim and Paula and the jobs at Concho were a blessing to the employees who went. Larry Gates, a drilling supervisor who had been at Henry for four years at the time, was on the Concho side of the split. "My time with Henry Petroleum was the best four years of my thirty-five-year career as a petroleum engineer. When Ronnie and Jim announced the sale and I learned that I was leaving Henry, I was obviously disappointed. However, in hindsight the sale was truly a win-win for Henry, for Concho, and for all the Henry employees, both those that went to Concho and those that stayed with the new Henry Resources." Larry stayed for his full bonus and went on to a successful tenure at Concho. "Jim and Ronnie selected the best possible company for the purchase of Henry. Concho was fully invested in the Permian Basin, from both a business and community standpoint. The company culture was hard work in a good atmosphere with generous compensation."

Forrest Collier went to Concho as well. Forrest, also an engineer, had joined Henry in 2006 and was working the FMEA project at the time of the sale. "The bonus was a life-changer for me. I was able to pay off the house, fund both of my daughters' college educations, and have some fun money left over." Months before anyone knew about a sale, Forrest and a few other employees were talking informally with Ronnie. "I remember him telling us that he wouldn't sell the company unless it was good for the employees. He delivered on this promise…The transition of Henry employees to Concho was designed for success. Many good former Henry employees went to Concho with the sale." Henry rehired Forrest two years later when the lock-up expired. "I resigned from Concho and went back to work at Henry in September 2010. I didn't leave Concho because I was unhappy. I was attracted back to Henry because of the people, culture, financial incentives, and the chance to participate in Henry projects."

The employees with interests in Henry properties again got a double whammy, in a good way, as Concho offered to buy them out at the same metrics that they paid for Henry Petroleum. The offers were made to those both staying and going. Those who accepted received eye-popping checks, most manifold larger than what they had reaped two years earlier at the Sweetie Peck sale.

In the wake of all that receiving came a lot of giving, as employees in turn blessed their families, churches and community. "It was very gratifying," Jim said, "when I found out later how much the employees passed on to others." Of course they passed it on—they were only following Jim and Paula's lead.

———————

Having blessed their employees, Paula and Jim turned their generosity toward Midland. "We especially wanted to share our wealth with the city that had helped us get started," Jim said. Shortly after the sale, they established a plan to give $10 million to local entities over the next five years. They funded the gifts not from the oil company but from their personal income, and before the end of the first year, they had donated more than $3 million to groups including their church, Casa de Amigos, United Way of Midland and a planned tennis center. In the end, Paula and Jim spread their $10 million over twenty-three local entities and two of Jim's Okie alma maters, Classen High School and the University of Oklahoma.

But the Henrys had already been planning a more permanent vehicle to perpetuate their philanthropy to the Midland community. They had begun creating The Henry Foundation in 2006, two years before the Concho sale was even envisioned. "But we could see that we were beginning to make some real money back then," Jim said, "and we wanted to start giving back." By the time the Henrys received IRS approval for their foundation, Ronnie and Danny were working on the company sale. Jim and Paula waited for its outcome, and when the sale closed the next summer, they donated their initial amount of $1,000,085. The Henry Foundation made its first gift the following year: the recipient, of course, was Casa de Amigos, Jim's philanthropic hometown.

As of 2021, The Henry Foundation's total giving is $25 million (in addition to the Henrys' personal philanthropy through the years). As in the beginning, the foundation is funded entirely by Paula and Jim personally, who contribute from the earnings they receive as owners of their oil company. To anchor their generosity in perpetuity, the couple has established an arrangement that, at their passing, will funnel their share of Henry profits directly into the foundation.

"Jim and Paula are absolutely the most generous people I know," Steve Owen said. He continued with a little hyperbole, but just a little: "The only work I ever saw Jim do was working at how to give away his and Paula's money. And I know Paula has a lot of input into that."

We humans never reflect the image of our Maker more clearly than when we are benevolent. The Henrys look a lot like Him.

Chapter 15
Transitions

So how do you follow that?

In Henry's five Wolfberry years, the company's headcount had quadrupled as its rig count quintupled. The team had drilled and completed 600 wells in the play, and a couple score more at other projects. At the time of the sale, they operated more than forty separate Wolfberry prospects, spread over fifteen counties, with total production (including non-Wolfberry properties) of 23,000 BOEPD. As a result, Henry's value had increased more than tenfold (net of the Sweetie Peck sale and Summit departure). This was the stuff of legend.

A repeat was out of the question. Henry was now much smaller, with fewer people and properties. The Wolfberry was much larger. A crowd of competitors had long since joined the play, and most of the big acreage blocks were leased and being drilled in development mode. Larger companies were now buying smaller ones for their acreage assets, just as Concho had bought Henry. There were smaller tracts left open, but most of these had issues: surrounded by larger tracts already taken, held by speculators demanding unreasonable terms or landowners not wanting to lease, or too close to homes, highways or businesses. For companies pursuing open tracts, the need wasn't for speed, as it had been when Henry kicked off the play, but for detailed assessment of risks and thorough development plans prior to signing. This meant slow going, which meant slow growth, which was not on Henry's agenda.

Henry couldn't repeat the blitz, but they could continue in the Wolfberry on a smaller scale. The team had acquired some acreage leading up to the sale, which they now owned in the new entity, Henry Resources. They could develop these, and they could also pursue the remaining small tracts. And there were two other possibilities for growth still within the Wolfberry. The team could test the outward limits of the play by drilling in the untested northern reaches of the Midland Basin. They could also test the inward limits. Recall that shortly prior to the Concho sale, Henry had drilled 40-acre wells in between the 80-acre locations and proven that, at least in some places, the infill wells were profitable. It was possible that wells drilled on an even tighter spacing of twenty acres would also be economic. The team went forward with all these projects.

As it turned out, Henry would slow to almost a standstill over the next five years. The team would find that both the external and internal limits of the Wolfberry were, in fact, already defined, and all the good remaining acreage taken. As a result, they would move on from the Wolfberry and attempt new plays, none of which would work well and some not at all. Henry would also experience a major management kerfuffle that would leave the company in disarray. In the midst of these trials, there was another successful sale. But in the grand scheme, Henry was headed for the doldrums.

Shortly before the sale to Concho, Henry had secured a few properties for the Henry Resources restart. They were just what was needed to reboot the downsized company. All were situated within the established Wolfberry fairway, so the geology and engineering practices were familiar. They were also very close to town, only a few miles from Henry's office. And each of the blocks was composed of either contiguous or checkerboard sections that enabled the operations team to erect efficient and cost-friendly infrastructure. They named the properties according to each one's principal landowner: Cowden East, Casselman-Bohannon (CaBo for short), and Nobles, about 25,000 acres in all.

What was not helpful was the low ownership interest Henry wound up with. Nawab, Henry's primary partner in the blocks, kept a majority interest, and each of the properties had other owners as well. When the operating agreements were signed, Henry had only about 15% ownership in the lot, which would make it difficult to build wealth in any reasonable timeframe.

The search for more leases in the heart of the play proved a challenge. The team learned after taking one tract that they would be unable to drill on it because the county had designated the surface for use as a cemetery. Another tract was occupied by a shuttered petrochemical plant at the center of a political dispute.

Not all the acreage was quite as difficult. Henry was fortunate to acquire a full section immediately north of the city, with its only issue being proximity to a residential area. They named the lease Robbie, and kept 100% ownership. This was a departure from Jim's routine of taking a partner to share risk. But because of the prospect's high potential and the need to offset low interests in the other properties, Henry kept it all in this case. At about the same time, they acquired a few leases in Upton and Andrews counties, in which they also retained high working interests. So, within eighteen months after the Concho sale, the rebooted Henry Resources had assembled some 20,000 Wolfberry acres with a good slate of locations to drill, albeit with mostly low ownership and sometimes with complicating issues.

Having gathered what they could within the proven trend, the team began poking around in the northern edge of the play. They acquired 32,000 acres in a scattering of blocks straddling the Andrews-Gaines border, which they called collectively LLB. The project was positioned well geologically, and although it was sparsely drilled, there was a handful of moderately productive wells across the area. LLB was singularly important, as it was the last remaining untested area of the basin-rimming Wolfberry trend. If Henry confirmed its potential, there would still be some room for expansion. But if the project failed, the play's extent would be capped, and its days numbered.

Henry again retained a high ownership in the LLB project, 50% in this case. They sold the balance to a partner in Houston, and committed to drill eleven wells. Operations spudded the first well in September 2009, and by year end had drilled ten of the required eleven. Notwithstanding its proper setting, the Wolfberry reservoir turned out to be poor quality. The project was a bust.

Now, with the outward limits of the play defined, there was nowhere to go but inward. As LLB wound down in summer 2010, Henry initiated a pilot project for 20-acre drilling. Demonstrating the profitability of 40-acre drilling had added significant value to the company in the sale to Concho. The team wanted to assess 20-acre drilling toward the same hopeful end. If the wells were successful, Henry would double its locations remaining to be drilled. They tested the concept definitively by drilling fourteen 20-acre wells at the Casselman lease north of town. Over the next two years, the company conducted two other pilots at different locations. The results were the same at all three projects: the 20-acre wells made only about half as much as the 40-acre wells, and were not profitable in any pricing scenario.

The Wolfberry's life was running out. Henry had established

the exterior limits of the play while probing the basin perimeter, and they had found a limit to the density of wells they could profitably drill in the interior.

For the moment, Henry continued drilling development wells at its established properties around Midland. But the company needed to find a new play. In fact, by the time the Casselman 20-acre pilot project was initiated, the team had already begun collecting acreage in a Devonian play that they hoped would be the next thing.

As they were gearing up for it, the process was interrupted by Ronnie's second epiphany.

In early 2010, Ronnie's cat got killed by a coyote. It's Midland, it happens. Ronnie was living in the Grasslands neighborhood on the city's northwestern perimeter—hence the coyote incursion—about a mile from the entrance to Henry's Nobles lease. He wanted to give his cat a proper burial, and as his residential yard with an irrigation system was hardly fitting, he drove to the lease that night and did the deed.

After the interment, Ronnie cruised pensively around the property for a while. As he subconsciously noticed the number of Henry pumping units, he had a dawning perception: "We've almost drilled too many wells here. We're about to drill ourselves into the quiet zone."

There were basically two types of buyers on the property acquisition spectrum at the time. On one side, growth companies wanted a lot of acreage with few existing wells, as their business model was to increase value by drilling the wells themselves, then make a profit by flipping the property. Income companies, on the other side, wanted a lot of producing wells with little undrilled acreage, as their model was to acquire a revenue stream that would provide something of an annuity. Ronnie's "quiet zone" was the middle part of the spectrum, for which there were no buyers. That night, he realized that Henry had developed Nobles to the point that they would no longer be attractive to a growth company, but still well short of an income buyer's target. Ronnie concluded, "We need to find a buyer now, because we don't want to spend the capital to finish drilling it into income status."

Ronnie asked Danny to help him identify a list of potential buyers, just as they had done two years earlier. But this time Henry would only be selling properties, and keeping all the employees. With employees off the table, this would not be a negotiated sale, as with Concho, but a "shotgun offering" with the highest bidder taking all. Danny identified twenty candidate buyers, but Houston-based Linn Energy particularly caught his eye. Linn was on the income side of the acquisition spectrum. They had gone public in 2006, and entered the Permian Basin with two acquisitions in late 2009. The company was doing things differently than some of their production-acquiring peers: they were willing to take some undrilled locations, believing that they could generate more value with a little drilling. In the end, Henry received seven bids. Linn's offer of $305 million was highest because, as anticipated, they valued not only the existing production but the undrilled acreage as well.

The deal was done on April 1, 2010, Henry's third nine-digit sale in four years. Once again, Paula and Jim shared their largesse with all the employees, and once again extended it even to some contractors. Henry's consulting frac guru, George Miles, was among the recipients: "I was floored by that. Their generosity is something special. Contractors never receive anything like that anywhere else in the industry that I've seen. The fact that they cared about me, when I wasn't even an employee, was really awesome."

It could seem at this point that selling had become the norm at Henry—Sweetie Peck in 2006, Concho in 2008, and now Linn in 2010, with a few smaller divestments along the way. After the

Concho sale, Jim had emphasized that "we are not going to sell every two years," as he and Paula wanted to be a legacy oil company and to retain legacy properties. But, he had qualified, "I want it clear, though, that we're not above selling, when the time and price are right. But from now on, we will ensure that our employees are kept."

With the closing of the Linn sale, Henry was in a situation similar to the one after Concho. They had a small number of low-ownership properties—some of the same ones, in fact, having excluded CaBo and Cowden East from the Linn sale. They were operating only seventy-four wells producing a combined 1300 BOPD, and, due to their low ownership, only 150 of those daily barrels belonged to Henry.

But there was a watershed difference between post-Concho and post-Linn: the Wolfberry was now on the wane. The profitable play limits were established, confined internally to 40-acre drilling and externally to western Midland and Upton counties. Interestingly, the endpoints of the geographic sweet spot turned out to be the company's first two property areas, Sweetie Peck and Chickadee—Henry had found the best stuff first. All that remained was infilling the play to 40 acres. A lot of companies were hard at it, and the Wolfberry's expiration date was all but fixed.

Wins in the material world can be seen and measured, and the Wolfberry was a fantastic win by the tangible metrics of barrels and dollars and jobs. But there are also matters of the heart. Wins in this realm are immeasurable and invisible, and sometimes invaluable to those who achieve them. The archetypal dream of every true oilman and woman is to be part of a major find, and the Wolfberry was that find for the Henry folks. As Jim said when the Caitlin and Beverly wells both came in at over 100 BOPD, "We had been looking for something like this for our entire career, and we had finally found it. We were very euphoric!"

When I asked Gary Pitts what he considers his most significant accomplishment during his time at Henry, he said, "Being the initiator and negotiating the deal with CMS that led to the Wolfberry—that just tickled me plumb to death! Then doing the same thing with BP for Sweetie Peck and so on until we had over 200,000 acres before anyone else knew what we were doing." Gary Elander answered along the same lines: "I've got to say, being an integral part of the start and development of the Wolfberry play. It never dawned on me in my previous twelve years at Henry that we were going to be anything more than Henry, just a great family company staffed by decent people trying to do the right thing. I got a clue when we went from 30 people to 130, and I did feel like something was changing when our yearly bonus suddenly had another zero added on to it. But I could never have predicted how incredibly this all worked out for all of us."

Bob Howard was not an employee, but the company's long-time wireline provider and later its consultant in the play. "You asked if I had an epiphany [of how big this play was going to be], and I did. It took a while to get there. Somewhere around 2007, I realized that this thing is so much bigger than anything I ever understood. When I think of Mr. Henry," Bob said, "I think about him drilling little Spraberry wells, having a program at the end of every year. And then he grew into this company that has meant so much to the employees and to Midland and the Permian Basin, and it's just phenomenal." At one point early in the play, Mike LaMonica had suggested that Bob become a Henry employee himself. Bob let the opportunity pass. "My only regret was that I think I could have gotten a full-time job at Henry. I should have accepted it—Mr. Henry takes pretty good care of guys that work for him."

Dave Feavel, one of the four visionaries of the Wolfberry, talked about the enormous wealth the team created for the entire community—the jobs, family income, tax money for cities and counties that funded schools and hospitals, and the largesse paid forward in altruism at every level. "I find real satisfaction in all that."

Doug Smith was concise as usual: "I was humbled and honored to have worked on a big stage at Henry." Keep in mind that Doug previously worked for multi-national behemoth Exxon, yet he sees Henry's Wolfberry epic as the true "big stage."

Mike LaMonica was hired by Getty Oil out of college in the late 70s to work as an engineer in their Tulsa office. In the lobby of the building hung a large, old, black-and-white photograph of famed oilman William Skelly and his managers, proudly hoisting a geological map of an oil discovery. Greenhorn Mike was moved by the picture: "I thought, 'Man, I wish I could have been a part of an historical discovery like that.' But when I started in the late 70s, everything had been discovered, there wasn't anything left to discover. Every field I worked on at Getty had been found back in the 50s or 60s. I thought I was never going to be a part of something historical." But then came the day at Henry in early 2003, when Mike was summoned to a meeting where Gary Pitts and Dave Feavel had something to show. Here was a team of oil company managers gathered, and here was a large geological map pinned to the wall. Mike's mind—and heart—went straight back to the Skelly photo. "I knew when I saw Dave's map with a 150-mile-long trend outlined on it that this was a big deal and I was going to be a part of it. It made me feel great!"

At the time of the Linn sale, with the Wolfberry fading, Henry had to make some hard decisions and go-forward plans. They could no longer dance with the one that brought them: it was time to change partners.

By Jim's watch, it was about time for a change anyway. At some moment in the previous decade, Jim had added a new ism to his list: "The strategy that got you through the past seven years won't take you through the next seven." The ism was a recent addition because it had been born from Jim's long experience. Throughout his business life, he had observed that the companies that survive are the ones continually looking ahead for the next thing, even while riding the current wave. This had proven true for his company as well. Sometimes the change was imposed by outside forces, and the company made use of the opportunities presented. Other times Henry proactively planned and created innovations. In any case, the company had morphed a time or two every decade to this point: Jim started in the Spraberry in 1971, attempted the Austin Chalk and Appalachia in 1980, waterflooded Phoenix Grayburg in 1987, made MIPs and secondary units in the 90s, and pioneered a great new play during the first decade of the new millennium. Now, in 2010, Henry still had many locations left to drill on its vintage Wolfberry acreage, and the team would even land a few new Wolfberry leases within the next two years. But this was basically mopping up, and would not suffice to grow the company. Henry needed a next thing.

Exploration manager Craig Corbett had suggested the Devonian formation as a candidate. While at Oxy, Craig had explored and drilled Devonian wells around the Central Basin Platform, where the reservoir had produced a prodigious amount of oil through the years. All the large fields had long since been discovered. But Craig had made a couple of moderate finds, and he still had some undrilled ideas in his head when he came to Henry. He thought the Devonian might be the new dance date Henry was looking for.

The team began identifying and leasing Devonian prospects in late 2009, still months prior to the Linn sale. At first, they acquired a handful of small tracts in Ector and Winkler Counties, and then a larger lease in Crane, which they called the Block 31 prospect.

There, they drilled the first two Devonian wells in summer 2011. The early results were good, but not grand. The team watched the wells produce for about eight months, at which time it was clear that the reserves would at least meet Henry's financial metrics, and they began developing the prospect. The initial drilling at other Devonian prospects soon followed, but the results there were not as good. Perhaps Henry should keep looking for another date.

As Henry was transitioning the development machine to Devonian prospects in the spring of 2012, the company management team was in transition as well. David Henry, Paula and Jim's son, was in his mid-thirties by this time, and managing his own investment shop. He was enjoying himself and doing well, but he also wanted a hand in controlling his share of the family's oil wealth. David and his parents began talking about how he might lead the oil company. Meanwhile, Ronnie had proposed reformatting the company leadership toward the kind of management-team structure typical of companies backed by private equity firms. Jim was against it, so Ronnie contemplated other solutions. And Terry Creech, Jim's executive financial counselor, was also in the mix. After diversifying the family wealth following the Concho and Linn sales, Jim placed Terry over the newly created investment side of the business. As an accountant, Terry was thinking along the lines of a traditional family office structure for the company, with a small staff, more diversified investments and some form of non-operated position in oil and gas.

So, three men—David Henry, Ronnie Scott and Terry Creech—were lobbying for different changes in Henry's organizational structure. After weighing all their options, Jim and Paula revealed their decisions in the summer. They set up David as CEO of the oil company, and positioned Danny Campbell as president under him. Ronnie voluntarily resigned his post as president of Henry Resources and moved to the other end of the building, where he would create and lead a second Henry oil company,

HPC. The new company would be entirely distinct from Henry Resources, funded by Jim and Paula's alternative investments, and a portion of its profits would be funneled into the Henry Foundation to fund the couple's philanthropic purposes. A small team of Resources technical types was agreeably reassigned to assist Ronnie at HPC. For the moment, Terry remained as CEO of the Henrys' investment side. Jim and Paula threw the startup switch on this new arrangement in August.

Reorganizing a business is like remodeling a house: the results cannot be fully envisioned until the actual changes have been put in place, and some issues won't become apparent until the new version has been lived in for a while. At that point, the owners might consider a second round of changes—and down the road, often a third.

The problems with the new arrangement became clear almost immediately. David was dissatisfied with his role. Yes, he was CEO of the oil company, but his decisions still required approval from Jim and Paula. And his sisters, who were also owners, had different financial priorities and risk tolerance that also needed to be honored. David wanted to call his own shots for his own wealth, and he began to talk about taking his share of the estate and going out on his own.

HPC had its own difficulties, beginning with the fact that Henry Resources and HPC were bound to begin competing. This was not lost on Midland's business community, who often brought it up with Henry employees: "So Jim has *two* oil companies now—how's that working for him?" There were internal problems as well. Henry's accounting team was working for both companies, so they now had twice as much to do. Loy Helm, Henry's CFO, recalled that "our workload just exploded. We had two sets of everything. I was going to two different managers' meetings all the time. It's like I had two jobs. And two masters. At the end of the day, who did I answer to?"

Ronnie was still unable to persuade Jim to set up a private equity-style management team structure at HPC, and Terry still wanted more say in the company's affairs. The employees in the engine room were disquieted by the obvious dissension on the bridge. Most importantly, Paula and Jim were displeased with the complexity, confusion and unrest the reorganization had created.

Fortunately for everyone, the arrangement didn't last long. In March 2013, only six months after the rollout, Jim and Paula enacted a second set of organizational changes to restore peace in their family and order in their company. They agreed that David should withdraw his share of wealth from the family estate and start his own venture. "We know our son better than anyone else," Jim said. "We knew he needed to be on his own in business." The family worked with Terry and Loy to separate David's allocation, and he established his own enterprise in the following months. Also, Jim and Paula wanted one oil company, not two, so they dissolved HPC. With the end of HPC, Ronnie decided to leave and start his own oil venture. He exited in July, and the HPC team opted to leave with him.

Terry was now the ranking manager in the organization, and Jim and Paula appointed him CEO of the whole company, over both the oil and investments sides. They also made him president of the investment side, and they moved Danny back to the oil side as president of Henry Resources. When the reorganizational smoke cleared in the summer, there was an accountant at the top of the Henry pyramid. In a traditional family office setup, this might work. But for a company with a fully staffed oil operator as the centerpiece, the arrangement was tenuous.

At the time of the first reorganization, Henry was having only limited success in the Devonian prospects. They drilled three more prospects at about the time of the second, and the results were decidedly bad. While still searching for the next big thing, the team had been fortunate to land two Wolfberry prospects. The first, Melinda, was a single-section tract in Upton County owned by Henry's cousin, Summit, which had drilled only eight wells to that point. The Henry team wanted the property for its potential in the remaining Wolfberry locations and in the deeper Bend formation, and they negotiated an equitable transaction with Summit.

The second prospect came as an unsolicited offer from Chevron, Henry's old WCJV partner. The Henry team—David Bledsoe and Craig Corbett in particular—had kept alive the relationship with Chevron after the two companies parted at the Concho sale, and now their efforts paid off. Chevron owned a 3100-acre block straddling both I-20 and highway 191 east of the airport, that was geologically well situated for Wolfberry potential. But it was very near the airport, highways and several businesses, and some of the acreage could only be accessed by drilling directionally. (In a *directional* or *deviated* well, the surface location is placed some distance away from the intended bottom-hole location; the hole is drilled vertically downward to some point, then angled off at a slant to reach the planned TD.) Chevron management preferred not to operate in close proximity to such culture. But based on their WCJV experience, they were confident that Henry could develop the block safely. Bob Heimke, Chevron's team leader, asked David and Craig if Henry would like to make a proposal for developing the block? Negotiations began soon afterward, and the two companies reached an agreement a few months later. The Henry-Chevron gang was riding again. And because Henry was happy to be back in the saddle, they named the prospect *BITS*.

BITS and Melinda were welcome projects to the Henry team during the Devonian failures and management melee. But they were finite, and did not present the sort of running-room potential that the company needed for long-term growth. The team had continued casting about for alternative opportunities, and acquired two prospects that were way outside Henry's wheelhouse. Carta Blanca was a street deal peddled by a local prospector. It was very large and far away: 19,000 acres in northwestern Terrell County, about 150 miles from Midland. In addition to the obvious operational difficulties this presented for Henry, the project also had geological and engineering risks. Henry's old dance partner, the Wolfcamp, was the main pay target. But this was a very different Wolfcamp. Here, the formation was not shale and limestone but fine-grained sandstone, and the reservoir contained not oil but gas (technically, *gas condensate*). Consequently, all aspects of the play, from its geological character to its marketing needs, were new to the team. Henry took the deal anyway, basically hoping against hope that a multi-stage, slickwater frac would be the magic key to unlock the prospect's reserves.

The other deal was also from the street. End Run was logistically similar to Carta Blanca, about 18,000 acres straddling the Pecos-Terrell County border, 150 miles from Midland. The deal was not only encumbered with hefty terms, but, most critically, its intended target zone was not at all well-defined. The summary presented at Henry's employee election meeting stated that "there are multiple objectives at the End Run Prospect, from Leonard and Wolfcamp shale to more conventional reservoirs including Canyon sands, Penn Detrital, Woodford shale, Devonian chert, and Connell sands. It is a large acreage block with good past production history that our modern stimulation techniques should improve." In other words, the team was going to throw it all at the wall and see what stuck, again hoping that the slickwater frac would cure all ills.

Henry inked Carta Blanca and End Run in spring 2013 as the second reorganization was being rolled out, and soon began drilling several test wells. In short, both projects were big-time busts. In hindsight—which of course is 20/20—the risks attached to both deals should have dissuaded Henry from taking them on. These uncharacteristic moves evince the disorder at the top of the company and the disorientation trickling down through the ranks. The same goes for the Devonian program, which the team continued to drill in spite of the fact that only two of the prospects were yielding profitable returns.

For about three years, since the time of the Linn sale in 2010, Henry had been drifting. The team had attempted to chart courses along a few different headings, but these had proved to be doldrums. Fortunately, hope appeared on the horizon. Literally.

Danny Campbell returned to Henry's oil side as president in August 2012 during the first reorganization. He convened a meeting with his technical team on his first day, and issued a mandate: "We *will* become horizontal competent!" During the next eighteen months, while Henry's vertical prospects petered out one after another, the staff worked diligently to climb the horizontal learning curve. By the end of 2013, they were ready to go sideways.

Chapter 16
The Horizontal World

HORIZONTAL DRILLING IS just what it sounds like.

A hole is first drilled vertically downward to within a few hundred feet of the target formation. The Wolfcamp in the central Permian Basin occurs at about 10,000 feet, so the vertical segment of a Wolfcamp horizontal well is about 9500 feet deep. Then the bit is *kicked off* at an angle to begin the section of the wellbore called the *curve*. The angle is gradually flattened out, until the bit is *landed* horizontally in the target formation. From that point, the hole is drilled laterally to a predetermined length. These days, the typical length of the lateral portion of the wellbore is from two to two and a half miles (10,000 to 12,500 feet).

The actual mechanics of drilling a horizontal hole (also called a *lateral*) are straightforward in the general. Once the vertical part of the hole is drilled, a *mud motor* is installed in the drill string behind the drill bit. The mud motor is designed with a slight kink in the body of the tool. Skipping the technical details, a mud motor allows the bit to be rotated while the drill pipe is stationary, and the kink in the tool allows the bit to be steered in a curve. Modern *measurement while drilling* technology (MWD, which includes GPS), also installed downhole, allows the bit to be precisely located and steered in three-dimensional space. And by the way, ordinary drill pipe is plenty flexible to accommodate the curve and lateral dimensions described above.

The advantage of drilling horizontally, rather than vertically, is that horizontal drilling exposes more reservoir to the wellbore. Imagine a shale layer that is 100-feet thick from top to bottom and extends laterally for hundreds of square miles. A hole drilled vertically through the zone contacts only 100 feet of it, but a hole drilled horizontally for two miles in the same zone contacts 10,000 feet. The effect is that more oil is rendered in close proximity to the wellbore, and can therefore be produced more quickly. In the shale layer just described, an oil molecule located 1000 feet away from a vertical wellbore must be pushed (by reservoir pressure) through 1000 feet of low-permeability matrix in order to be produced. That takes many years at least. But a horizontal hole can pass right by that molecule, making it instantly available for extraction. And now consider a molecule 10,000 feet away from the vertical hole: given the shale's low permeability, that droplet has no chance of ever being extracted. But with a 10,000-foot horizontal hole drilled close by, there's no problem getting it out of the ground.

The contemporary multi-stage fracturing technique hugely compounds the accessibility effect of a horizontal well. In today's slickwater frac designs, perforation clusters are positioned about every twelve feet along the full length of the horizontal hole. When the well is fracked, the result is a series of fractures spaced twelve feet apart, each one extending a few hundred feet out from the borehole into the reservoir. This system creates a pervasive, three-dimensional network of passageways for hydrocarbons to travel into the wellbore. Without a frac, an oil drop that happens to be 100 feet from the borehole will traverse that distance very slowly through low-permeability shale matrix. But with a multi-stage frac, the drop is likely to be within six feet of a fracture, through which it can be quickly flushed into the wellbore for production.

The benefit of a fractured horizontal hole is therefore twofold: a much greater volume of oil is accessed and produced than in a vertical wellbore, and at producing rates that are much higher. For comparison, CMS's early Wolfcamp tails wells produced at initial rates of 75 BOEPD, and made about 60 MBOE in thirty years. Today, a 10,000-foot Wolfcamp lateral will initially make 1500 BOEPD and produce 750 MBOE in the same amount of time. Granted, a horizontal well costs more to drill and complete than a vertical, but the incremental gain far outweighs the incremental cost.

There are also environmental benefits to horizontal drilling. Because horizontals drain a reservoir so efficiently, a single well can take the place of ten vertical wells. The result is a smaller surface footprint: fewer well sites, tank batteries, power lines and roads. That geographic benefit is multiplied in that many horizontals can be drilled from the same well pad, with the surface holes being as near as thirty feet from each other, while the horizontal boreholes below the surface spread out over a much wider area. This means less of a lot of things, including pollution, manpower, time, danger, materials and cost.

As with fracking, horizontal drilling is nothing new. The first attempts in both the US and overseas date from the late 1920s, and these were few and unsuccessful. Then in the early 1980s, mud motors (described above) were developed that significantly increased the ease and accuracy of directional drilling, and operators began experimenting. The first systematic testing was carried out by the French company Elf Aquitaine in 1980–83. Later in the 80s, BP began experimenting with horizontals in Prudhoe Bay, Alaska.

As the horizontal process improved and gained popularity, operators began searching for other applications. Drillers in the Austin Chalk play realized in the mid-80s—right after Jim left—that by drilling horizontally in a direction perpendicular to the trend of existing natural fractures, they could intersect multiple fractures rather than the single one they might encounter with a vertical hole. The attempts were largely successful at increasing rates and reserves, and a play took off. In September of 1987, Meridian Oil (aka Burlington Resources) drilled and completed the first horizontal Bakken shale well at the Elkhorn Ranch Field in Billings County, North Dakota. Although the Bakken shale is geologically different from the Chalk limestone, both formations are naturally fractured, and this early Bakken play was basically the same as the Chalk play. Neither the Chalk nor Bakken operators hydraulically fracked their wells in these formative years; they only relied on intersecting natural fractures while drilling.

In the Permian Basin at this time, operators began drilling horizontally in *conventional reservoirs* (strata with moderate to high porosity and permeability) in shallow carbonates on the shelf and platform. Here, their goal was to penetrate more reservoir, and thereby increase rate and reserves, as described above. By the 90s, this style of horizontal development was common. Some companies then began horizontally developing reservoirs down in the basins on both sides of the platform. On the Midland side, majors drilled Devonian horizontals at existing giant structural fields—Texaco at Bryant G, Mobil at Parks and ARCO at Pegasus. And recall that CMS, spurred on by Danny Campbell, entered the horizontal Devonian play in 1999.

Even Henry Petroleum dipped a few toes into the horizontal pool during this time. In late 1999, Henry established its small and complicated Marathon MIP at Olson Field. While scouting for projects, the team identified a zone in the upper San Andres that they believed was being insufficiently drained by the existing vertical wells. They determined to re-enter a vertical hole, the Shannon M-1 #20, kick off at 1995 feet using a *whipstock* (a plug with a slanted top to establish angle) and proceed to drill a 500-foot lateral. The "simple" job took more than a month to complete, and supplied the hardship appropriately helpful for such a first-time event. In the end, they succeeded in drilling and completing the lateral, but it failed to increase production.

Henry dipped a second toe eight months after the Olson attempt, this time for a much deeper target. Azalea is a Devonian gas field in northeast Midland County, originally discovered and drilled vertically in the 1960s. In late 1997, local oilmen Ted Collins and Herb Ware got the idea to drill Azalea horizontally, believing that the vertical wells had not sufficiently drained it. They bought some leases, and struck a partnering deal with a large oilfield service company to test the concept. The partner spent $20 million drilling and completing four, one-mile laterals. Combined, the wells initially produced a non-whopping total of 165 BOPD, 1300 MCFGD. It turns out that the reservoir had been drained effectively, and the project was a bust.

In the spring of 2001, some other local oilmen tied up leases in the vicinity of Collins & Ware's debacle and brought Henry management the very same idea. Despite the troubled history and some internal advice against it, Henry committed to drill one horizontal Devonian well on the prospect. The Sarah #1H, named for Ronnie's daughter, spudded on August 8, 2001. This well also had its requisite share of problems, and took sixty-nine days to drill 12,000 feet down and 4300 sideways. The result was, predictably, disappointing: 23 BOPD plus 197 MCFGD on the official completion report. This was not a money maker, and Henry cut its losses and sold the project four months later.

———————

At the beginning of the new century, these early horizontal plays in naturally fractured and conventional reservoirs were beginning to align on a trajectory that would soon result in the so-called "shale revolution." Horizontal drilling doesn't get all the credit, though. Nor does multi-stage slickwater fracking, nor shale. All three components—shale reservoir, horizontal borehole, slickwater frac—are necessary to make the play and must be present to win. Interestingly, all three components were well known by the early 2000s, and each of the early plays was enlisting one or two of them, but none of the operators saw the sea-change potential of the three combined.

Some operators came close. In the late 80s, UPRC used slickwater fluid in the Austin Chalk to pump multi-stage acid stimulations. But the Chalk is a limestone, not a self-sourcing shale, and an acid job is not a frac. Meridian drilled and completed the first horizontal Bakken shale well near the same time, but they were only looking for existing natural fractures, so they did not hydraulically frac their wells. In 1990, the Department of Energy funded a research project in West Virginia with PrimeEnergy Corporation and the Gas Research Institute, in which they drilled diagonally (not quite horizontally) through the Huron shale, and fracked it in four stages. But instead of using the new slickwater design, which was likely still unknown to them, they used compressed nitrogen, then the frac fluid of choice for Appalachian shale operators. The results were no better than traditional vertical wells, and no one followed up. Finally, Mitchell Energy in 1997 experimented with UPRC's slickwater frac design in the Barnett Shale, but only in vertical wells.

It is not clear when and where the three components came together for the first time. Information about a well's *direction* (vertical, deviated or horizontal) and producing formation is available from state agency records, as these parameters are required reporting, so we know where and when horizontal wells were first being drilled in shales. But until recently, agencies did not require operators to disclose information about the frac recipe. Not that operators necessarily kept their ingredients secret. UPRC, for example, had published the successes and failures of their slickwater designs. But there was a lot of experimenting by a lot of operators at the time, and much of it was seat-of-the-pants practice that no one bothered to report. By the late 2000s, in any case, the shale-horizontal-slickwater combination was a going concern. In the oil portion of the play, a couple of Williston Basin operators were deploying the tri-combo in the Bakken shale in North Dakota; and in the gas portion, Devon Energy and others were developing the Barnett shale in the Fort Worth Basin. Similar horizontal plays were blooming around the country, in shales including the Eagle Ford in South Texas, the Fayetteville in the Arkoma Basin and the Marcellus in Pennsylvania. Not all the operators in these plays used the same recipe for the slickwater frac—there are still variants today—but they were consulting a similar cookbook.

The Permian Basin was behind the shale curve at the time, although horizontal operators had begun to test potential in other conventional reservoirs down in the basins. On the Midland side, Parker & Parsley (and then Pioneer, after the merger with Mesa in 1997) began drilling occasional Spraberry laterals in the STA in 1996, primarily in Midland and Reagan counties. Operators on the Delaware side similarly began horizontal development in conventional Wolfcamp and Bone Spring pay zones around the same time. Horizontal activity on both sides of the platform increased slightly over the next few years, still with all the effort directed at established conventional reservoirs.

But then EOG did something different. The company was carrying out CEO Mark Papa's order to identify and develop what he called "resource plays"—that is, drilling horizontally in *un*conventional reservoirs, such as ultra-low permeability shales and siltstones that had previously been thought non-productive. His team had already gained horizontal shale expertise in the Barnett and the Bakken. In late 2009, EOG applied its learning to the Wolfcamp in the Midland Basin. They acquired acreage, not near the shelf where the vertical Wolfberry play was established, but out in the basin, in southwestern Irion County, where the sediments are finer-grained and organic source material more abundant. They landed their laterals in a shale zone in the upper part of the Wolfcamp, and their early results were promising, if not glamorous.

EOG's activity immediately caught the attention of other operators, and soon Devon, EP Energy and Petrohawk engaged in the play, and expanded it into Crockett and Reagan Counties. By the end of 2011, there were 130 horizontal Wolfcamp shale wells in the area. In 2012, other operators pushed the play westward into Glasscock, Upton and Midland counties, drilling more than 330 wells in that year. Laterals grew longer and fracs larger, and wells in both the Wolfcamp and Spraberry shales were routinely completed at producing rates of more than 1000 BOEPD. Ultimate reserves were estimated in the neighborhood of 750 MBOE per well.

The shale revolution had arrived in the Permian Basin, and it was at just this time that Danny Campbell issued his horizontal challenge.

Chapter 17
Henry Goes Sideways

HORIZONTAL WAS NOT new to Danny Campbell. While at CMS in the late 90s, he had drilled some thirty laterals, most of them in the Devonian formation. This was the conventional horizontal play, as explained in the previous chapter. Later, at Henry, when he was relocated to the investment side in 2010, he kept tabs on the oil community: "I was kind of looking over the fence at the industry, watching what was going on." He had watched EOG introduce the unconventional horizontal Wolfcamp shale play to the Midland Basin, and now he saw many operators joining the movement.

Danny's oil friends kept him apprised of these developments. "A lot of people who had asked us questions about the vertical Wolfberry in the Henry glory days were returning the favor now, and telling me what was going on horizontal-wise." Steve Gray, founder and CEO of RSP Permian, was particularly helpful. "Steve and his team had earlier asked for Henry to share some vertical information on the fracs we were doing. And because we had given that information to them, they began sharing their horizontal details with us." The early shale results were good, even though the operators were still on the steep part of the learning curve. And because of the "layer cake stratigraphy" of the Wolfcamp and Spraberry Formations—shale intervals within them are laterally continuous for hundreds of square miles—it looked as if the play would extend across several counties. "Based on RSP's and other people's results, I knew the next stage for Henry had to be horizontal."

But first, they would have to rebuild the drilling department. When HPC was formed in the first reorganization, prompting Danny's return to the oil side of Henry, Ronnie Scott and Michael Rhoads went with the new venture, leaving only Blake Braun and Doug Smith in the drilling group. Doug had a long resume of accomplishments on drilling rigs. But his only horizontal experience was on Henry's Sarah one-off a decade earlier. "That was the first time I'd ever been around any of it, so I was green as a gourd when it came to this stuff."

Blake was in his mid-20s with only a handful of drilling years behind him, but Danny thought he could handle management. They determined to try it for a few months, and if he did well and wanted the position, Danny would give Blake the big seat. "I think he wanted to see if I would freak out," Blake said. He passed the test, and became drilling manager in what he called a "battlefield promotion" as his entire chain of command had recently evaporated. "They took a risk putting me in a position that I wasn't really qualified for. But it was the turning point in my career, having that responsibility and learning how to figure out what was required."

Blake scheduled meetings with engineers at other companies who knew the horizontal world, and went to school on them. And he literally went to school, at K&M Technology Group, a consulting and training firm that provided a two-week short course on the rudiments of horizontal drilling. Others on Henry's technical team boned up on the horizontal world as well. Craig Corbett and his team quizzed their geological network about identifying appropriate shale targets, and engineer Forrest Collier tapped his contacts on the reservoir and completion front to learn the latest horizontal fracking methods and recipes.

The team selected the CaBo prospect for Henry's first horizontal shale well. The vertical production there had been consistently good, and they figured the horizontals would be, too. There was a lot of horizontal activity in the area at the time, and here was an opportunity to make Henry's low CaBo ownership work for, rather than against, them: the team would be risking only a dime on a dollar for their initial horizontal education. The group chose section 36 on the western side of the Bohannon block for the drill site. The lease was a single section, and consequently they would be limited to a lateral length of about 5000 feet. At the time, that length was standard for the area, and they did not want to reach too far on the first try anyway.

Henry's team and their consultants created a well plan for the Bohannon36 #1H—the "H" signifying a horizontal well: they would drill a 9300-foot vertical segment, kick it off on a northerly azimuth, and bore a 4500-foot lateral in the upper Wolfcamp. They figured thirty days to drill plus a few weeks to complete the well and put it on production, and they estimated the total cost at $7.3 million. Danny approved the AFE for Henry, the partners approved it for themselves, and the team was finally ready for Henry's inaugural horizontal shale venture.

It all went sideways from there.

———————

The bad omens began even before the well spudded. The drilling team had retained a custom-tailored rig for the venture, and would also be using *top-drive* equipment for the first time. Blake had hired "a hotshot drilling consultant" to superintend the operation, a man with vertical and horizontal expertise, recommended by industry contacts. Because of all the new elements, Blake and Doug decided to put the rig, crew, top drive and consultant together on a vertical well first, so they could work out the kinks and get used to each other, before moving to the horizontal.

Everything went well during the drilling operation. But on the morning the crew began to run casing, Doug arrived to find that the consultant had not been on the rig floor at all during the previous night. When Doug asked why not, the crew said the man had gotten drunk in his trailer. "So I called Blake, and we got the drug boys out there and pee-tested him, and he was still hot then. So we fired him on the spot." And with that inauspicious start, the rig, crew and top-drive equipment—but not the consultant—moved on to the Bohannon36 #1H.

The well spudded shortly after noon on December 4, 2013, and the drilling went fine through the vertical and curve segments. But as they were drilling ahead on Christmas Day, a few hundred feet into the lateral segment, the on-site consultant—the *replacement*—began to unravel. As with the first guy, the second guy had been highly recommended. But no one mentioned that he didn't play well with others. "He was just a hothead," Blake said. "He disagreed with what we were doing and what the rig crew was doing, and he was literally coming apart at the seams, causing all sorts of problems with our team on location." After trying to control the man by phone for several hours, Blake finally drove to the rig—"at three in the afternoon, right before Christmas dinner," Blake lamented—and fired him. The Bohannon well clearly didn't like contract drilling consultants. And the timing of the firing was a bit of a tactical error: Doug was on days off over the holiday, and Blake had to take the man's place and spend Christmas night on the rig.

The training project was just warming up. As the crew continued to drill the lateral, the penetration rate became slow, much slower than industry contacts had told the team to expect. Whatever rock they were drilling was harder than the soft shale they had targeted. At 3:25 a.m. on New Year's Eve—the well apparently didn't like holidays either—the drill pipe got stuck. They were almost three-quarters of the way done with the lateral. Blake remembers the call from the crew: "It was in the middle of the night, when things always happen on a drilling rig. And that was the beginning of a slow-motion train wreck."

They tried for days to dislodge the pipe, but nothing worked, and the costs kept cha-chinging at a rate of a hundred thousand dollars per day. Blake felt the pressure spike. "It just felt like the worst possible thing that could have happened was happening. The voices of the imaginary naysayers were echoing in my head: *We can't do this. We don't know what we're doing drilling horizontal wells.*"

Blake and Doug finally gave up trying to free the pipe, and decided to sever it and *sidetrack* the lateral (back up the hole, angle out of the existing borehole and drill a new one beside it). They tried twice to cut the pipe in the lateral, using a standard method. Both attempts failed. The team then tried to assess the downhole situation by lowering a special tool into the wellbore on wireline. That tool also got stuck. And when they attempted to sever the wireline from the tool, in order to retract the line from the hole, the cutter malfunctioned and triggered at the surface. Now they had 13,000 feet of drill pipe stuck in the hole with 13,000 feet of cable stuck inside it, along with miscellaneous metal debris. As Blake put it, "Now we were fishing for our fishing tools. I remember spending a lot of days and nights in the trailer out there. We didn't sleep a whole lot for about two weeks, and we couldn't sleep even when we had the opportunity."

But dawn appeared at the bottom of the dark. "I was at my wits' end at one point, and Danny called Doug and me into the office because we were pretty much out at the rig 24/7. We gathered everyone up, and everybody was calm. It was serious, but it was, like, 'We're gonna fix this, we will figure it out. So what's the plan?' It was reassuring for me to see that we were fighting it as a team.

That's just the character of Henry, up and down through the ranks. Calm is sort of the fabric of the company. We're not screamers and yellers and people that put pressure on other people to get results in a situation like that." Clearly, Henry had grown up considerably since the Old School butt-chewin' days.

The light continued to brighten, and the team was finally able to cut the pipe at 10,700 feet, just past the heel of the lateral. They sidetracked the hole, and reached total depth on January 22 and cemented casing two days later. The drilling phase of the project had taken fifty-one days, almost twice as long as planned.

For the training project to be effective, everyone had to share in the misery. The drilling team had taken its beating. The completion team was next up.

Early in the morning on Valentine's Day, George Miles met the completion ensemble at the location—crews from the frac, wireline, water transfer and sand-hauling companies, along with all their machinery and equipment. For weeks, George and Forrest had been meeting with the players, separately and together, rehearsing the details. Now it was time to perform. They held the pre-job safety meeting at 6:45, and started pumping the first frac stage a half an hour later. It went off without a wrinkle. One down, twenty to go. By George's assessment, for the next five days and seventeen stages, the job went "pretty smooth overall."

At the start of the day on February 19, there were three stages remaining. The Henry team had wanted Jim and Paula to visit the location for the historic frac job, and as this was anticipated to be the final day, Roy Madison loaded them up and chauffeured them the short distance from town to the site at mid-morning. The couple toured the operation while the wireline crew was prepping the well for stage twenty, then left around 11:00.

Just fifteen minutes later, with the well now perforated, they revved up the pumps and the frac commenced. George remembered: "We were almost done with the whole job. We were in the frac van, talking about how we were getting pictures of everybody when we finished up. We were already kinda doing our high-fives. But then, when the [pumping] rate reached about 60 barrels a minute, we heard this loud *BANG!*" The master valve on the wellhead, through which the frac fluid was being pumped down the wellbore, broke and instantly slammed shut. "The pressure spiked to 13,000 pounds on a 10,000 pound-rated line. Everything failed. A couple of lines blew off the wellhead. Several connections parted. Stuff flew all over location." By grace alone, no one was hurt.

George shut down the operation for the day to assess the damage and determine the cause. The next morning, with new safety measures in place, everyone resumed their stations for stage twenty, take two. This stage and the next were uneventful, and at 8:00 that evening George entered a note at the end of his report: "Job complete."

Well, not quite. The frac plugs had to be drilled out, and the well placed on production. With the drilling and frac teams in the clubhouse, the operations group now warily approached the first tee.

The cleanout part of the operation went flawlessly. But when the crew tried to install the downhole equipment necessary to produce the well, the whole assembly got stuck at about 9300 feet, right at the top of the curve. And as in the drilling debacle, they were unable to detach the wireline from the stuck tools. They did manage to sever the wireline from the tool using a downhole cutter, but then the cutter itself broke, and remained in the hole when they retrieved the cable. Once again, they were fishing for their fishing tools. The crew made two attempts to fish the cutter, but on each attempt, more stuff broke off in the hole. Forrest and Doug decided to try to retrieve the tools with tubing, instead of grappling for them with wireline. That began a full month of frustratingly failed attempts. "Bad memories!" Forrest said. "The fishing job was all-consuming for about four weeks. We had already been through so much with this well—drilling issues, the frac valve breaking, all that stuff. The fishing job was insult to injury."

They eventually retrieved everything except for one tool that kept slipping farther down the hole when they tried to grind it up with a drill bit. Enough was enough. Forrest and Doug gave up and placed the well on production as it was, hoping that the lost tool wouldn't clog it up. The well flowed for a month at a moderate rate of 300 BOPD. Then the team ran a downhole pump and officially completed it on April 6. From spud to completion, the well had taken four months of continuous effort. The horizontal training project was officially over.

In the final analysis, Henry's first attempt at a horizontal shale well was not profitable. At least not financially. "I don't recall what the AFE was," Doug said, "but we spent all the money up front on that dude." When the hemorrhaging was over, the total cost was $8.6 million, about $1.3 million more than planned. Seven years later, the well has made only 144 MBOE—not even close to paying back its investment. Happily, only a few months after the completion, Henry sold the property to Callon Petroleum, who paid the going horizontal premium for the whole acreage block, as they intended to drill it all laterally. Still, from a purely investment perspective, the well was a loser.

And those most intimately involved with the well also paid an emotional price. Blake called it "a slow-motion train wreck," and Doug "a freakin' train wreck"—apparently train wrecks were to the Bohannon horizontal what *Indiana Jones* was to the Wolfberry play. George referred to it as "a disaster," and Forrest labeled it "a nightmare." And these are strong men.

But money isn't everything. And no pain, no gain. For only a dime on a dollar and four months' worth of blood, sweat and tears, the whole Henry team had purchased an excellent education in horizontal drilling. "It was probably the best money spent," Danny said, "because it was great training. Like Jim says, 'Hey, you're not making mistakes unless you're doing something.' We had issues, but we learned from them and turned around and became very competent. And that's a real Jim Henry-type story." Blake expressed a similar view: "You learn through trial and tribulation sometimes more than through success." In contrast to these philosophical perspectives, George's takeaway was purely pragmatic: "Now we don't do any high-fiving until it's completely finished and the valve is closed!"

Not everyone saw blessing in the Bohannon. The experience all but depleted Doug. "That was kind of the start of my finish. Not just that well but the horizontal work in general. I could see that's where I was going." Doug was not a young man, and his forty-plus years in the industry had been spent mostly outside in the West Texas elements. He had made a lot of difficult decisions in the middle of the night on the floor of a drilling rig. The horizontal world was shaping up to be even more demanding. "The intensity of the workload that I knew I was going to be faced with… You gotta have a big fire built up for that. You gotta have a lotta want-to. And I started running out of steam."

With their training complete, the team now evaluated Henry's existing prospects for horizontal potential, even though all of them had been originally acquired only for vertical development. They identified a second location three miles southeast of the first one, and spudded it two months after the first was completed. The plan for this second well was in all ways similar to the first—same pay zone, lateral length and frac design. The project was blessedly uneventful. The well was drilled and completed in a total of 51 days, less than half of the Bohannon's 123, and the spending came in under budget. All measurements were moving in the right direction.

For its next horizontal project, the team selected the Woodford shale at Henry's Block 31 Devonian prospect in Crane County. The Woodford there is very similar in some ways to the Bakken shale at the prolific Elm Coulee Field in Richland County, Montana. No Woodford horizontals had been drilled in the vicinity, but the team believed the zone had potential and wanted to give it a lateral try.

Henry spudded the UnivTaylor #192UW in late October. It took the team only 14 days to drill the vertical hole and the curve, set intermediate casing and begin drilling the lateral. They were clearly hitting their horizontal stride, even in this geologically uncharted territory. Then, the geology pushed back. The limestone landing bed, less than twenty feet thick, left no margin for steering error, and any deviation would allow the unstable shale encasing it to cave in. The drilling rate slowed to a crawl, and then halted, as all the crew's time and effort were spent shoring up the hole rather than drilling it longer. After four days without any forward progress, the team decided to stop the lateral where it was, at 4200 feet, just more than half of what was planned—better to test the Woodford concept with a short lateral than risk no test at all.

In the end, the well was a proverbial "geologic success but economic failure." After peaking at 120 BOPD, production dropped to 20 and assumed a low decline. The team lamented the economic failure, celebrated the technical success and filed away the learning for future opportunity.

Henry drilled two more horizontal wells that year, both on the Melinda lease acquired from Summit. That brought the first-year sideways total to five, proof that the team was resolutely set on becoming "horizontal competent." They were not content to drill only their existing properties, but searched for new horizontal opportunities as well. They landed two projects in the southern Midland Basin in early 2015. The first, Trinity, was a huge block of 64,000 acres in Crockett, Reagan and Upton counties. The property had been previously owned by ConocoPhillips, who had drilled eleven unsuccessful horizontal Wolfberry wells there. Henry believed that with better pay targets and contemporary methods, they could make profitable wells. The second prospect, BSG, was a 7300-acre block in northcentral Crockett County, where the Wolfcamp is relatively richer in gas than oil. The team began drilling both prospects in the spring. In the end, neither made Henry much money, but the operations did help them become more horizontally proficient.

The BITS partnership with Chevron near the Midland airport proved much more profitable. The original BITS arrangement had not contemplated horizontal development, but now Chevron and Henry agreed that laterals would make the most economic and effective sense going forward. In June 2015, Henry drilled two laterals there, both about a mile long and landed in the Lower Spraberry Shale. Although the laterals were short, the production results were very profitable for the partners. Henry continued to develop the prospect, and, as of 2021, had drilled thirty-four horizontals there.

By the end of 2015, the Henry staff had fulfilled Danny's horizontal mandate. They had spudded the first horizontal well sixteen months after the edict was issued, drilled five laterals in the first year, and in the next two years thirteen more. By then, the problems they were experiencing were simply the routine cost of doing business in the horizontal world. Henry was not a pioneer in this world, as they had been in the vertical Wolfberry play, but they were a fast follower, running hard on the heels of the leaders. Henry had become horizontal competent, and the team set about using their new skill to grow the company to the next level.

They are well on their way. At the writing of this chapter, in June 2021, Henry has drilled a total of 107 horizontal wells. The cumulative footage for these wells is 1,702,070 feet—that's 358 miles, the same as the distance from Midland to Plano. These horizontals have produced a combined 20 MMBOE, and their yield will grow steeply in coming years: eighteen of the wells have only been completed within the last twelve months, and several are still waiting to be brought online. And new reserves will be tapped as the team adds new horizontal prospects to the queue and drilling continues at a pace.

The success of Henry's horizontal program is due not simply to excellent reserves, but to the compounding effect of horizontal efficiency and higher working interests. A good horizontal well makes eight to ten times the rate and reserves of a vertical well. This efficiency is manifest in Henry's current producing well statistics: the company currently operates 170 producers, split about evenly between horizontals and verticals. But even with only 50% of the well count, the horizontals make 98% of the production. There are also overhead savings: fewer wells require fewer employees for drilling and maintenance. And since taking the presidential reins in 2017, David Bledsoe has maintained a practice of retaining high working interests. While Henry has kept as much as 75–100% ownership on a few horizontal prospects, David explained that "our sweet spot is about 40%. That works very well on all of Henry's financial metrics."

The results are much improved even over the company's stellar past performance, seen clearly in its current producing rates. On a gross basis, Henry is producing almost exactly what it was making at the Concho peak in mid-2008, about 23,000 BOEPD. But owing to the higher working interests, the company's net production is 8600 MBOE—80% more than the 4800 BOEPD at the Wolfberry peak. Again, this benefit is compounded by horizontal efficiency: ignoring the vertical wells, which contribute an insignificant amount of current production, the team is now producing about the same gross rate with 88 horizontals that they were producing then with 950 verticals—that's only 9% of the well count. And the company is achieving this feat with less than half of the personnel—58 now versus 127 then (employees and contractors). David was not casting hyperbole when he claimed that "we are truly in a new era for Henry."

———————

Two properties contain poignant markers of the vertical world Henry left behind. At BITS, the Denise #1610 spudded in January 2015 and was completed in September, just as the prospect's first two laterals were being fracked. This was a "changing of the guard" moment, as the Denise was Henry's final well in the vertical Wolfberry play that had promoted the company to "the big stage."

Henry continued drilling vertical wells at its Devonian prospect in Crane County during the few years following the Wolfberry end. There, in early 2019, the company drilled its last vertical well, the UnivShannon #1805. The end was symbolic. When the operations team attempted to place the well on production, they found the casing parted below the top perforations. They spent three months and $600,000 trying to salvage it, but to no avail. The well was never completed.

Since then, Henry has been horizontal one hundred percent.

Epilogue
Now We Are Fifty-Two

IN THE COVID spring of 2020, within days of oil prices bottoming out in negative territory and the world looking like it would end, the Henrys called an employee meeting to issue a very clear communication: "You do not have to worry about losing your jobs." Jim and Paula have held firmly to their resolve never again to lay off for financial reasons. They even gave the employees a bonus that year. Not huge, but meaningful, not only for its financial value but for the example of generosity even when times are tough.

Today, the Henrys are reaping the fruit of their long labor and benevolence. Shortly before the company's 50th anniversary celebration, Jim jumped out of an airplane for a celebration of his own—his 85th birthday—following the lead of his friend, the late President George H. W. Bush, who parachuted every 5th birthday. Jim started skydiving in his late 70s, and he intends to jump again on his 90th (although Paula says otherwise). Now approaching 87, Jim is active at exercise and still loves to play tennis. When I met him recently for lunch, I perfunctorily asked how he was doing, and he, very non-perfunctorily, replied, "I'm really having fun!" Paula and Jim continue to enjoy philanthropy through their foundation and from their personal wealth, and they spend much of their time pursuing their most beloved avocation—their grandkids.

Although Jim seldom involves himself in Henry's day-to-day affairs, he remains very much engaged in the larger matters. He loves the oil business, but he is not necessarily wedded to it. He is watching the transition toward cleaner energy and sustainability with interest. Wind and solar are making progress, but because these energy forms are so "dispersed," as he describes them, they will always be cost-prohibitive: "The poor countries can't afford the green energy because it costs too much to harness and condense it for use." But he is attracted to the potential of nuclear energy, which is not only clean but *denser* than any other form of energy, which makes it the cheapest energy on the planet—even cheaper than oil and gas. Many experts and innovators, Bill Gates among them, are advocating for nuclear development and funding projects using new nuclear technology. I asked Jim how he would feel if, in the future, Henry pivoted from fossil fuels to nuclear energy. "I'd feel great! But I wouldn't feel great if they went into wind and solar."

I finally asked Jim what he wants for Henry in the next fifty years? He answered quickly—this is something he thinks a lot about: "What I'd like is for the basic principle of our company to continue: I want us to be a Christian company. This is extremely important to me. It is what drives us, what is at the heart of our company. We 'do unto others as we would have them do unto us,' and we always try to 'love our neighbors as ourselves.'" He clarified his motivation for adhering to this standard: "We are a Christian company because we believe it is the right thing to do, not because we will make money by doing it. And we don't treat other people well so they will treat us well—that doesn't work. We treat other people well because that is what the Bible tells us to do." Above all, that means rewarding the folks who work for them: "Being a Christian company entails being very considerate of our employees, who do all the work in getting the wells drilled. So the employees should always get a large share in the profit." And he wants to keep sharing the profit with the Midland community as well: "I would like to continue to have the foundation give back to the city that's helping us create all this success." Consequently, Jim wants the company to remain private, because a public company could never achieve these ends.

I pointed out to Jim that in response to my question, he had answered—true to form—with precepts for goodwill, rather than with business objectives. But what about business goals for the next half century? What are the "something different every seven years" projects that he wants the company to work on? Should it continue in oil and gas? Shift to nuclear? "Oh well, those are questions that'll have to be answered by the people who are working for the company at that time. They'll have to figure it out."

So there it is, Henry employees of the future: you have your assignment.

AUTHOR'S ACKNOWLEDGEMENTS

I have had the great privilege of working for Jim and Paula Henry for more than twenty years. The Henrys are very special people, as the entire Permian Basin will attest, and I was deeply honored when they asked me to write a history of their company. Their story is a good one, and I hope I have told it well.

I don't know why authors wait until last to credit their spouses, but as I'm not a real writer, I'll take a pass. I would not be a reader and thinker, would not be able to write anything meaningful at all, were it not for Rachel's cultivation of all things beautiful and good and true in our family.

I am grateful in the extreme to all my interviewees. Most of them were or are Henry employees, but some are linked to the company as friends, business partners or service providers. All were very giving of their time and happy to contribute. It is their story, too, and there would be no story to tell without them. These conversations are what I will miss most now that this project is finished. I interviewed a few of these folks multiple times, and once the actual interviews were concluded, I bothered them some more with follow-up emails and texts. Of course, I spent the most time with Jim, but, as the book was his idea, he brought it on himself. A close second place goes to Dennis Johnson, past president of the Henry company and founder of his own oil enterprise, Summit Petroleum. I took so much of Dennis's time that we almost had to put him back on the payroll. A little off the pace, but worthy of honorable mention, are Dave Feavel and Gary Pitts, two men essential to the making of the Wolfberry play. I needed to be certain that I understood their accounts and retold them accurately, and both gents were very patient in what may have been a painful process.

The entire roster of current Henry employees contributed to this effort in some way. They are good people and a lot of fun to be around, and I am fortunate to have them as my friends. Special thanks to George Miles, our completions superintendent, who happens to be handy with a camera and contributed some of his wellsite photos to the book, including the rig shot silhouetted on the front cover. Brandi Watkins, our financial analyst, was a great help in making digital copies of old pictures, and in taking original photos as well.

I am particularly grateful to the trio that served as my "handlers" while I was writing this book: Paula and Jim's executive assistant, DiAnn Barker, and the co-managers of the Henry company, David Bledsoe and Danny Campbell. All three acted as counselors and blockers: they advised me on matters above my pay grade, both corporate and familial, and kept my logistical path clear so I could continue working. They also provided necessary and excellent feedback, which rendered the final product more accurate and interesting.

Great thanks to my Big Apple editor, Sam Douglas, whose skilled and radical surgery cut away a mass of distracting wordiness, anecdotes and details, to ensure that the Henry story is heard clearly. Thanks also to Gary Sernovitz, a managing director at Lime Rock Partners (private equity investors in upstream oil and gas) and a real-deal writer himself, who encouraged me early and introduced me to Sam. I cannot adequately express my appreciation for Christina Delay, professional author and owner of Nimbus Brands, for guiding me—I'll be honest, *carrying* me—through the entire publishing process. (And thank you, Rebecca, for recommending your cousin to me!)

And mentoring thanks to my friend and accomplished author, Jimmy Patterson, who provided guidance at the outset that pointed me in the right direction.

Soli Deo gloria!

AUTHOR BIO

Gregory Berkhouse received a BS degree from the University of Texas and a MS from Indiana University, both in geology. He worked for more than a decade with Exxon Corporation in exploration and production assignments in the East Texas Basin, the Rockies, and finally the Permian Basin, where he cross trained as a reservoir engineer. He left Exxon for Collins & Ware, a Midland independent, to avoid a transfer to Houston, and when that company was acquired by Apache Corporation a few years later, he left again for the same reason. He joined Henry Petroleum in 2000, where he participated in pioneering the Wolfberry play and later segued with the team into horizontal development. At some point along the way, he came to be regarded as a guy who might be able to write a decent book, if ever the need should arise.

Printed in the USA
CPSIA information can be obtained
at www.ICGtesting.com
LVHW021918101123
763491LV00033B/1663/J